CW00547500

50 Great Stories For Christian Kids

Bedtime Stories For Kids, Volume 1

Lila Rosewood

Published by Lila Rosewood, 2023.

50 GREAT STORIES FOR CHRISTIAN KIDS

First edition. July 18, 2023.

Copyright © 2023 Lila Rosewood.

ISBN: 979-8223984337

Written by Lila Rosewood.

Also by Lila Rosewood

Bedtime Stories For Kids
50 Great Stories For Christian Kids

Faith Warriors Chronicles
Divine Armory: Equipping For Spiritual Battles

Mompreneur's Journey: Empowering Work-from-Home Moms
The Mommy Flex: How To Create A Work-Life Balance That Works For You

Standalone
The Cheaters Antidote: Safeguard Your Relationship From Infidelity
Whispers Of Forbidden Love
Whispers Of Forbidden Love

Dedication

Dedication:

"To the young seekers of faith and the bright stars of tomorrow, this book is lovingly dedicated.

May these fifty stories become treasured companions on your journey of discovering the depths of your Christian beliefs and values. As you turn each page, may you find inspiration, guidance, and the warmth of God's love illuminating your path.

To the parents, grandparents, and guardians who strive to nurture a strong foundation of faith in their children, thank you for the unwavering commitment to fostering a deep connection with God. Your love and devotion provided the fertile soil in which these stories were sown, and it is my heartfelt hope that they will flourish in the hearts of your little ones.

To the tireless teachers, pastors, and mentors who selflessly pour their wisdom and guidance into the lives of young minds, your dedication to shaping tomorrow's faithful leaders is truly commendable. May these stories serve as valuable tools to reinforce the lessons you impart and deepen the understanding of our shared Christian beliefs.

Lastly, to the young readers who embark on this adventure of faith, may these stories become beacons of light, leading you closer to God's unwavering presence in your life. May they ignite your curiosity, instill a sense of awe, and kindle a lifelong love for the teachings and values of Jesus Christ.

May every page of this book radiate God's love and grace into your hearts.

In faith and with abundant love,

Lila Rosewood

The Adventures of Faithful Friends

Once upon a time, in the peaceful town of Hopeville, there were three best friends named Emily, Jonathan, and Sarah. They were known for their joyful hearts and their strong faith in God. Together, they embarked on incredible adventures, where they learned important lessons about their Christian faith.

In their first adventure, the trio discovered a mysterious book hidden in an old attic. As they opened it, they were transported back in time to biblical Jerusalem. They found themselves in the presence of Jesus, witnessing the miracles He performed and hearing His teachings firsthand. Overwhelmed with joy, they eagerly listened, took notes, and soaked up every bit of wisdom they could.

Returning home, Emily, Jonathan, and Sarah shared their newfound knowledge with their families and friends. They encouraged others to read the stories of Jesus, teaching them about love, forgiveness, and serving others selflessly. Their town became filled with the spirit of compassion and unity as more people followed Jesus' example.

As their adventures continued, the faithful friends encountered challenges and obstacles that tested their faith. In one adventure, they faced a fierce storm while sailing on the Sea of Galilee. Afraid for their lives, they cried out to Jesus for help, just as the disciples did long ago. In that moment, they learned to trust in God's power and experienced His peace that surpasses all understanding.

In another adventure, the friends discovered a lost sheep in the nearby mountains. Remembering the parable of the Good Shepherd, they embarked on a journey to find its owner. Along the way, they encountered obstacles, but their faith and determination led them to reunite the lost sheep with its grateful owner. This experience taught them the importance of seeking and caring for those who stray from their faith, just as Jesus does.

Throughout their adventures, Emily, Jonathan, and Sarah learned that prayer and worship were vital in their journey of faith. They would often gather in a small chapel to pray, sing praises, and seek God's guidance. Their time with God strengthened their friendship and deepened their faith, as they discovered the power of relying on Him in all circumstances.

As the book draws to a close, Emily, Jonathan, and Sarah realize that their adventures were only a glimpse of the countless stories and teachings found in the Bible. They encourage each other and their community to continue exploring and growing in their faith, knowing that a life centered on Christ is a life full of love, hope, and unimaginable adventures.

The Adventures of Faithful Friends inspires children to embrace their faith, study the Bible, and follow Jesus' teachings. It teaches them the values of love, compassion, forgiveness, and trust in God. Through the example of Emily, Jonathan, and Sarah, young readers learn that friendship and faith in God can help them overcome any challenges they may face.

The Little Seed's Big Journey

Once upon a time, in a vast field of green, there stood a little seed. It was small, humble, and filled with wonder as it looked up at the towering trees above. The little seed dreamed of growing tall and strong, just like the magnificent trees that surrounded it.

Day after day, the little seed watched as the wind carried its neighboring seeds away, on grand adventures. It wondered when its turn would come.

One sunny day, as the breeze danced through the field, it whispered a secret to the little seed. "Be patient, little one," it said. "Your time will come. God has a special plan for you." The little seed trembled with excitement, and from that moment on, it knew it must trust in God's perfect timing.

With each passing season, the little seed grew more eager to embark on its journey. It yearned to see the world beyond the field, to reach up towards the sky and touch the fluffy clouds with its branches. But it continued to wait, trusting that God's plan would unfold in due time.

One rainy afternoon, the little seed felt a gentle tap on its shell. The raindrops, like tiny messengers, were urging it to break free from its protective covering and embrace the adventure that awaited. Encouraged by their rhythmic patter, the little seed pushed and pushed, until finally, a tiny sprout emerged from the soil.

As the days turned into weeks, the sprout grew taller and stronger. It stretched its tender leaves towards the sun, soaking in its warm rays. With every passing moment, the little seed marveled at the beauty of God's creation and the care that had been taken to help it grow.

But just as it began to find its footing, a harsh storm raged through the field. The wind whipped and the rain poured relentlessly. The little seed trembled, fearing that its dreams would be swept away with the torrential downpour.

In that moment of turmoil, the little seed heard a calming voice whisper through the storm. "Hold on, dear little seed," it said. "I am with you." The seed clung to those words, finding solace in the midst of chaos. It trusted that God would protect and guide it through every trial.

As the storm subsided, the little seed stood tall, having weathered the hardships. It gazed up at the trees it once admired, realizing that it, too, had become a mighty tree. From its branches, birds nested and sang sweet melodies, and its shade provided comfort to all who sought refuge beneath it.

The little seed had learned the essence of true trust in God. It understood that its journey had not been arbitrary, but carefully designed with a purpose. It had learned that in the waiting, in the storms, in the growth, God had been at work, shaping it into something beautiful.

With great humility, the mature tree bowed its branches in gratitude, offering praise to the One who had nurtured it along the way. It shared the story of its journey with all who came near, spreading hope and inspiration.

And so, the little seed's big journey came full circle. It had transformed from a tiny seed filled with dreams to a mighty tree, standing tall and strong. It understood that God's plan was far greater than any it could have imagined.

As the little seed's story traveled through the fields and beyond, it encouraged others to trust in God's timing, to embrace the storms of life, and to grow in faith, knowing that just like the little seed, they too had a purpose and a unique journey to embark upon.

The Lost Sheep

In a peaceful village nestled between rolling green hills, there lived a young shepherd boy named Caleb. From the time the sun rose until it rested behind the horizon, Caleb cared for his father's flock of sheep with love and diligence.

One bright and sunny day, as Caleb counted the sheep, his heart sank. One was missing—Asher, his favorite sheep, had wandered off in search of lusher grass. Caleb knew he couldn't rest until he found Asher and brought him safely back to the flock.

With determination in his eyes, Caleb set off on a journey through the hills and valleys, calling out Asher's name. He searched tirelessly, climbing rocky slopes and wading through babbling brooks, hoping to catch a glimpse of his lost sheep.

Meanwhile, the other sheep graze contently, oblivious to the absence of their adventurous companion. Caleb's father, sensing his son's distress, joined in the search, leaving the other shepherds to watch over the flock.

Days turned into weeks, and Asher remained elusive. Caleb's heart grew heavy, and doubts began to cloud his mind. "Why am I putting so much effort into finding just one sheep? Aren't the rest important too?" he wondered.

As the sun began to set one evening, Caleb sank to his knees on a grassy hillside. His face streaked with tears, his voice trembled as he poured out his heart to God. "Please, Lord, help me find Asher. I don't want him to be lost. But I also need to understand why he's so important to me."

In that moment of surrender, a calming presence enveloped Caleb. He felt a deep sense of peace and heard a gentle whisper in his heart, "Every single one of my sheep is precious to me. Seek Asher with the same love and dedication as I seek each one of my children."

Renewed in spirit, Caleb rose to his feet and continued his search, not just for Asher, but for the understanding of God's unwavering love. As the days passed, Caleb's love for his lost sheep grew stronger, mirroring the boundless love God holds for His people.

Finally, after weeks of searching, Caleb spotted a fleck of white in the distance. It was Asher, his beloved sheep, tired and weak but safe. Caleb gathered Asher in his arms, tears of joy streaming down his face as he whispered, "You were lost, my friend, but now you are found."

Returning to the village, Caleb rejoiced as the townspeople gathered around to celebrate his miraculous find. Word of his journey and the value he placed on each sheep spread like wildfire, touching the hearts of young and old alike.

Caleb learned that day how God rejoices when even one of His lost children is found. He discovered the immeasurable worth of every individual, just as Asher was precious to him. From that day forward, Caleb vowed to share God's unconditional love with everyone he met, reaching out to those who felt lost and showing them the way back to the loving embrace of their Shepherd.

And so, the story of the lost sheep echoed through the generations, reminding people of God's love and their inherent value in His eyes. Caleb's journey taught him the importance of seeking the lost, holding them close, and never underestimating the power of love.

The Kind Heart

Once upon a time in the small town of Harmonyville, there lived a young girl named Lily. Lily had a heart filled with kindness and a genuine desire to help others. She was known for her warm smile and gentle nature. Lily's days were spent going to school, playing with her friends, and spreading happiness wherever she went.

One sunny day, a new student named Jenna arrived at Lily's school. Jenna had made some mistakes in her past, which had led her astray from the right path. As a result, she often felt isolated and judged, having difficulty making friends. Lily noticed Jenna's struggle and, driven by her own kind heart, decided to reach out.

Approaching Jenna with a smile, Lily said, "Hi, I'm Lily. I noticed you're new here. Would you like to join me and my friends during lunchtime?"

Jenna looked up, surprise and gratitude shimmering in her eyes. She hesitated for a moment before accepting Lily's invitation, realizing that this kind-hearted girl was extending a hand of friendship without judgment.

As days turned into weeks, Lily and Jenna became inseparable friends. They laughed, shared stories, and supported each other through ups and downs. Lily listened without judgment as Jenna opened up about her past mistakes, and Jenna began to feel a sense of acceptance and understanding that she hadn't experienced before.

One day, as they sat together under their favorite tree by the playground, Jenna shared her deepest regret with Lily. "I wish I could undo the mistakes I made in the past, Lily... Sometimes, it feels like I can never truly move on from them."

Lily looked at Jenna with compassion and said, "Jenna, we all make mistakes. What's important is to learn from them and grow into better versions of ourselves. Everyone deserves a second chance, including you."

Lily's words resonated with Jenna, planting a seed of hope in her heart. Jenna realized that friendship with Lily had brought her a sense of forgiveness and acceptance that she had never felt before. Lily's unwavering support and kindness had taught Jenna the power of love and understanding.

Inspired by Lily's example, Jenna began to make amends for her past mistakes. She started by apologizing to those she had hurt, genuinely seeking understanding and forgiveness. Some people were initially hesitant, but they saw the transformation in Jenna's character and gradually came to embrace her change of heart.

As time went on, Jenna's journey of growth and redemption continued. Lily stood by her side, providing guidance and support. Together, they emphasized the importance of forgiveness and kindness in the school community, starting a movement of understanding and acceptance.

Word spread about Lily and Jenna's friendship, and their story touched the hearts of many in Harmonyville. Students began showing compassion and forgiveness, learning from Lily and Jenna's example. The school became a place of unity, where everyone felt valued and understood, regardless of their past mistakes.

Lily and Jenna's friendship also influenced their families and the wider community. People saw the power of forgiveness in action and started reaching out to mend broken relationships and find common ground. The entire town of Harmonyville began to embrace a culture of kindness and forgiveness.

As the years passed, Lily and Jenna remained steadfast friends, inspiring others around them to embrace forgiveness and kindness. Their journey together taught them the importance of looking beyond mistakes and seeing the potential for growth and change in every person.

Harmonyville became a town known for its kind-heartedness, where second chances were given freely, and forgiveness was cherished. Lily and Jenna's friendship became a symbol of hope and a reminder that true transformation and healing were possible through forgiveness and genuine human connection.

In the end, Lily and Jenna's kind hearts sparked a ripple effect that transformed a town, proving that forgiveness and kindness have the power to heal wounds and build bridges between people of all backgrounds.

The Joyful Song

In the vibrant town of Harmonyville, a group of friends named Emma, Liam, and Sarah shared a deep love for music. They would often gather in their favorite park, singing songs and harmonizing with their voices intertwining in perfect unity. Their joyful melodies echoed throughout the town, spreading warmth and happiness to all who heard.

One sunny day, as Emma, Liam, and Sarah gathered near a blossoming cherry tree, Emma had an idea. "Why don't we start a choir, where we can sing together and share the joy of music with others?" she suggested, eyes shining with excitement.

Liam and Sarah eagerly agreed, envisioning a space where the whole community could come together to sing and experience the power of worship and praise.

They wasted no time bringing their idea to life. They spread the word around town, inviting people of all ages and backgrounds to join. Soon, their choir began to take shape, with members embracing the opportunity to share their love for music and faith.

At their first practice, the air was filled with anticipation. Voices of various pitches and timbres blended together, guided by Emma's gentle guidance and Liam's skilled piano playing. Sarah, filled with enthusiasm, lifted everyone's spirits with her infectious laughter.

As they practiced each week, something remarkable began to happen. The joy they felt while singing together multiplied and spread, touching the hearts of everyone present. The choir members found solace and inspiration in the music, discovering that their voices had the power to create an atmosphere of unity and love.

In preparation for their debut performance, the choir chose a meaningful hymn that celebrated God's love and the beauty of creation. The harmonies rose and fell, weaving together like a tapestry of emotions. As the music filled the room, the audience witnessed a deeper connection unfolding among the members.

With each word and note, the choir experienced a sense of spiritual fulfillment. They realized that their voices were instruments of praise, capable of igniting hope and healing in their own lives and the lives of others.

When the day of the performance arrived, the church's pews were filled to capacity. Friends, family, and community members eagerly gathered to witness this display of unity and joy. As the choir took their places and began to sing, their voices seemed to soar with a newfound strength and confidence.

People in the audience closed their eyes, absorbing the melodies that brought comfort and solace. Others softly tapped their feet in time with the rhythms, feeling a sense of peace and tranquility. Tears of joy filled the eyes of those who felt the genuine spirit of worship and praise radiating from the choir.

Throughout the town, the impact of the Joyful Song choir continued to ripple beyond that initial performance. Harmonyville became a place where music and faith intertwined, where joy was celebrated, and where voices lifted in unity filled the hearts of all who inhabited the town.

Inspired by the choir's unwavering spirits, other groups began to form, spreading the melody of love, joy, and faith to neighboring towns. Word of the transformative power of music and worship spread far and wide, touching the lives of countless individuals who yearned for a sense of belonging and spiritual connection.

Years went by, but the Joyful Song choir remained an integral part of Harmonyville's fabric. Emma, Liam, and Sarah continued to lead with love, passing down their harmonious legacy to younger generations.

Their original vision had blossomed into something beyond their wildest dreams. The Joyful Song choir served as a reminder that when voices come together in worship and praise, hearts are transformed, joy is multiplied, and unity is forged.

In Harmonyville, the Joyful Song choir would forever be celebrated as a beacon of light, reminding everyone that through music and unwavering faith, the power of oneness and joy could be experienced by all.

The Giving Tree

In the heart of a lush forest, there stood a magnificent and giving tree. This tree, with its strong branches and towering presence, had a kind heart and a spirit of generosity that extended far and wide. For years, it had provided shelter, nourishment, and playfulness to the creatures that called the forest their home.

Children from the nearby village had often sought solace beneath its welcoming shade and had enjoyed swinging from its sturdy branches. They delighted in climbing up its trunk and embracing the tree's comforting presence. This brought joy to the giving tree's heart, for nothing brought it greater happiness than seeing others happy.

As the seasons changed, so did the needs of the forest inhabitants. In the winter, when the forest creatures struggled to find food, the giving tree shared its acorns and provided a sanctuary among its leaves, shielding them from the biting cold winds. In the spring, the tree blossomed with vibrant flowers, spreading a sweet fragrance and attracting bees, who benefited from its nectar.

One summer day, as the sun shone brightly overhead, a young girl named Lily ventured into the forest. She wandered aimlessly, her heart heavy with worries. Sensing her distress, the giving tree gently beckoned Lily to come closer. With each step, Lily felt a sense of peace envelope her. The tree whispered in a gentle breeze, "Do not be troubled, my dear child. Bring your worries to me."

Lily sat against the tree's trunk, her head nestled against the bark, and spoke of her troubles with tear-filled eyes. She conveyed her fears, anxieties, and burdens to the tree, which listened compassionately, offering its strength and understanding.

Moved by Lily's vulnerability, the tree knew it had to help her. It said, "Lily, my child, take these leaves as tokens of my love and care. Whenever you're feeling down or in need, place one of these leaves under your pillow at night. It will bring you peace and remind you of the unconditional love that surrounds you."

Grateful tears filled Lily's eyes, and she embraced the tree with a tight hug. She promised to cherish the leaves and share the tree's message of love and selflessness with others.

Word of the giving tree's magical leaves spread throughout the village. People approached the tree, seeking comfort, and received leaves as a symbol of its love and generosity. The leaves became a reminder that, just as the tree provided for others, they too had the power to give and share their blessings with those in need.

As the years went by, the tree continued its benevolent mission, embracing all who sought solace, support, and love. It showed the forest creatures and the people of the village the importance of selflessness and giving, just as God provides for us.

One autumn day, the tree stood tall and proud, its branches adorned with colorful leaves. The forest animals gathered, along with the villagers, to celebrate the tree's unwavering generosity and its impact on their lives. They sang songs, shared stories, and expressed their gratitude for the tree's selflessness.

In the twilight of its existence, the aging tree embraced its destiny with grace. Its branches weakened, and the leaves fell, providing nourishment to the earth. The tree's spirit, however, lived on in the hearts of all those it had touched.

The villagers honored the tree's memory by planting saplings throughout the village, nurturing them with love and care. The seedlings grew tall and strong, continuing the legacy of the giving tree and inspiring future generations to selflessly share their blessings with others.

And so, the story of the giving tree became a cherished tale in the village—a reminder that through acts of selflessness and love, we can emulate the blessings bestowed upon us by our Creator. Just as the giving tree had shared its gifts, the villagers embraced the spirit of generosity and strove to create a world rooted in love and kindness.

In their hearts, the village knew that the memory of the giving tree would forever live on—a beacon of compassion and a reminder that when we give of ourselves, we receive far more than we could ever imagine.

The power of prayer

In the peaceful town of Serenityville, there lived a young boy named Daniel. Daniel was known for his vibrant imagination, zest for life, and his unyielding faith in the power of prayer. From a young age, he had been taught about the importance of connecting with God through heartfelt communication.

One evening, as the sun began to set, Daniel found himself facing a daunting challenge. His beloved dog, Max, had fallen ill, and despite the efforts of the veterinarians, Max's condition showed no signs of improvement. Daniel's heart ached at the thought of losing his faithful companion.

Discouraged but not defeated, Daniel closed his eyes, clasped his hands tightly together, and began to pray. He poured out his concerns and fears to God, asking for a miracle to heal Max and bring him back to full health.

Days turned into weeks, and Daniel's prayers for Max's recovery continued. With each passing day, his faith grew stronger, even as Max's health deteriorated. Daniel fervently believed that God was listening, and he held onto that hope with unwavering conviction.

One sunny morning, as Daniel sat by Max's side, something miraculous happened. Max, who had been weak and lethargic, suddenly perked up. His tail wagged, his eyes regained their sparkle, and he stood on all fours, as if a surge of newfound energy had coursed through his body.

Amazed and overjoyed, Daniel knew deep in his heart that his prayers had been answered. His faith had moved mountains, and God had extended His healing touch to Max.

From that day forward, Daniel's perspective on the power of prayer was forever changed. He recognized that prayer was not just a one-way conversation but a powerful connection with the divine. It was a way to seek comfort, guidance, and solace in times of need.

Throughout his life, Daniel continued to witness the incredible power of prayer. He prayed for others who were sick, for those who faced difficult circumstances, and for peace and harmony in the world. And time and time again, he saw how the prayers, offered with pure intentions and unwavering faith, evoked miracles and brought about positive change.

Daniel shared his experiences with others, encouraging them to approach prayer with an open heart and unyielding faith. His stories of answered prayers uplifted and inspired those around him, instilling within them a newfound belief in the extraordinary strength of prayer.

As the years went by, Daniel's own faith journey deepened. He grew to understand that even when prayers seemed unanswered, God had reasons beyond human comprehension. It was in those moments of trust and surrender that Daniel found peace, knowing that God's plan extended far beyond his limited understanding.

Daniel's unwavering faith in the power of prayer became a beacon of hope for the town of Serenityville. Inspired by his example, many began to embrace prayer as a means of connecting with the divine, seeking guidance, and trusting in the perfect timing of God's answers.

And so, the story of Daniel and his miraculous experiences with prayer spread far and wide, touching the hearts of countless individuals. It reminded them that there was immense power in connecting with God through prayer and that faith had the ability to move mountains, heal the wounded, and bring about hope in even the most challenging situations.

In the heart of Serenityville, Daniel's faith-filled journey became a testament to the power of prayer—an enduring reminder that in times of joy, sorrow, or uncertainty, the path of prayer could lead to miracles and draw individuals ever closer to the loving embrace of their Creator.

The Armor of God

In the quiet town of Faithville, there lived two siblings named Alex and Mia. They were known for their strong bond and unwavering faith in God. One sunny afternoon, while exploring their grandfather's attic, they stumbled upon an old Bible with a worn-out bookmark tucked between its pages.

Curious, Alex and Mia opened the Bible and discovered a highlighted passage in the book of Ephesians. It spoke of the spiritual armor of God, which believers were encouraged to wear to stand strong against temptations and trials. Intrigued by its message, the siblings eagerly dove into learning more.

Over the next few weeks, Alex and Mia studied the scriptures carefully, absorbing the significance of each piece of armor. They learned about the belt of truth, the breastplate of righteousness, the shoes of peace, the shield of faith, the helmet of salvation, and the sword of the Spirit, which is the word of God.

Armed with this newfound knowledge, Alex and Mia decided to implement the teachings and put on the spiritual armor in their daily lives. They understood that just as a physical armor protects the body, the spiritual armor guards their hearts and minds, providing strength and resilience against the temptations and challenges they would face.

In their first test of temptation, Alex faced a situation where peer pressure began to influence his choices. Remembering the belt of truth, he held fast to his convictions, standing firm in the knowledge of what was right and wrong. As he spoke the truth with grace and humility, the power of the armor protected him from giving in to temptation.

Mia, on the other hand, encountered a moment of doubt and insecurity. Remembering the breastplate of righteousness, she remembered her worth in the eyes of God, who had called her to live with integrity and virtue. Embracing her identity as a beloved child of God, she banished the doubts, standing tall in her faith.

As they faced various trials, the siblings learned to rely on the shoes of peace, which allowed them to walk confidently, spreading love and harmony wherever they went. The shield of faith protected them from doubt and fear, as they trusted in God's goodness and provision even in the midst of challenges.

Donning the helmet of salvation, Alex and Mia found comfort and security in the knowledge of their eternal destiny, guarding their thoughts against negativity and despair. And armed with the sword of the Spirit, the word of God, they found guidance and strength, ready to share its truth with others.

With each passing day, Alex and Mia grew stronger in their faith, as the spiritual armor fortified their hearts and minds. They discovered that the armor was not only for their individual protection but also a means to encourage and support each other.

As time went on, their community noticed the siblings' unwavering faith and resilience. Others were inspired as Alex and Mia shared the lessons they had learned from Ephesians, encouraging those around them to put on the spiritual armor as well.

The town of Faithville transformed into a community of believers, united in their commitment to stand strong against temptations and trials. Each member, like Alex and Mia, embraced the spiritual armor and stood firm in their faith, supporting one another on their journeys.

Together, Alex and Mia became beacons of light, shining God's love and truth to those around them. They realized that the spiritual armor was not just an individual protection; it was an opportunity to be ambassadors of God's goodness in the world.

And so, the story of Alex and Mia's journey with the armor of God echoed throughout Faithville, inspiring all who heard it. It served as a reminder that in the face of temptations and trials, believers could find strength and courage by adorning themselves with the spiritual armor.

Their example encouraged others to embrace the teachings in Ephesians, standing firm in their faith and relying on the power of God's armor. With the armor protecting their hearts and minds, the town of Faithville thrived as a community of believers, ready to face any challenge and spread God's light in the world.

The Little Candle's Light

In a quaint village on the edge of the Enchanted Forest, there lived a little candle named Lumi. Lumi may have been small, but its flickering flame held a world of warmth and joy. Nestled on a windowsill, Lumi would watch as the day turned to night, the stars twinkling in the sky.

Lumi loved its cozy spot in the village, but deep down, it yearned for something more. It longed to bring light to the darkest corners of the world, bringing hope and joy to those who needed it most. Lumi knew that even the tiniest flame could make a difference if it shone with love.

One evening, the village was struck by an unexpected storm. Thunder roared and rain poured endlessly from the sky. Darkness engulfed the village, leaving its residents feeling lost and afraid. But in the midst of the chaos, Lumi's tiny flame flickered with determination.

Feeling an indescribable urge, Lumi rolled off the windowsill and onto the street. It ventured through the heavy rain, its little flame dancing with each drop that fell upon it. Lumi knew it had a purpose - to bring light to the darkness and hope to the despair.

As Lumi made its way through the village, it stumbled upon a small, cobbled alleyway where a young girl named Mia sat, shivering and feeling alone. Her tears mixed with the rain, her spirit dampened by the storm both outside and within her heart.

With a flicker of its flame, Lumi caught Mia's attention. She looked up, squinting through her tears, and gasped as she saw the little candle's light. A spark of hope ignited within her, and she reached out to take Lumi into her hands.

Feeling the warmth of Lumi's flame, Mia's heart began to lighten. She held Lumi close and whispered her troubles and fears into the candle's dancing light.

From that moment, Mia felt a sense of peace and reassurance. Lumi's small flame had filled her with the knowledge that she was not alone.

Together, Mia and Lumi set out on a mission to spread light and love throughout the village. They walked hand in flame, their light illuminating the path before them. As they encountered different homes, they shared their message of hope, one small flicker at a time.

Children who had been frightened by the storm found solace in the comforting glow that Lumi and Mia brought. Elderly residents, burdened by worries, felt a renewed sense of joy as the little candle's light lit up their hearts. The village slowly transformed into a place of hope and love, as Lumi's flame grew brighter with each act of kindness and compassion.

News of Lumi's light spread far beyond the village. People from neighboring towns began requesting visits, yearning for the warmth of the little candle's flame. Lumi and Mia responded with open hearts, traveling to those in need, spreading joy and reminding everyone of their role in sharing God's love.

As the years passed, Lumi's light remained bright, its message of hope echoing throughout the land. It taught children and adults alike that even the tiniest flame had the power to bring light to the darkest places, reminding them of the invaluable role they played in sharing God's love with the world.

And so, Lumi continued to wander, bringing light and love wherever it went. Each flame it ignited grew into a beacon of hope, changing lives one flicker at a time. The little candle's flame burned on, reminding children and adults alike that within their hearts, they too possessed the power to bring light to the darkness and fill the world with hope and love.

The Miracle Maker

In a small village nestled amidst rolling hills, there lived a young boy named Samuel. Samuel was known for his inquisitive nature and his unwavering faith. He would often spend hours listening to stories of miracles and wonders performed by Jesus. Samuel was captivated by the miracles Jesus had done, and a burning desire grew within him to witness such miracles himself.

One day, Samuel's village received news of a traveling preacher who claimed to have the power to perform miracles, just like Jesus. Excitement rippled through the community, and people eagerly gathered to witness this miracle worker in action. Samuel, his heart full of anticipation, joined the crowd.

The preacher, a humble man with kind eyes, began speaking with great authority and compassion. His words resonated in the hearts of the people, and they felt a tangible sense of peace and hope settle upon them. Amidst the crowd, Samuel's faith intensified, and he yearned to witness a miracle firsthand.

As the preacher concluded his sermon, a nearby wedding celebration caught his attention. Samuel watched with wide eyes as the preacher approached the hosts of the wedding party. Whispers passed through the crowd, as they wondered what miracle would be performed.

The preacher smiled warmly and softly spoke with the hosts. Within moments, Samuel's heart skipped a beat as he witnessed something extraordinary. Large stone jars, once filled with water, now overflowed with a vivid crimson liquid. The water had been transformed into the finest wine!

As the crowd gasped in awe, Samuel's faith soared. He witnessed, with his own eyes, the power and authority of the preacher's miracle. He marveled at the way Jesus had turned water into wine all those years ago, and now this preacher had done the same.

The miracle moved Samuel deeply, and he realized that Jesus' power knew no bounds. Inspired by what he had witnessed, Samuel understood that the miracles Jesus performed were not only a demonstration of his power, but also a testament to his love and compassion for humanity.

From that day forward, Samuel dedicated himself to sharing the stories of Jesus' miracles with others, especially children. He wanted them to understand the immense power and love that Jesus had poured into the world through his miracles.

Samuel gathered the children of the village and shared the story of the water turning into wine. He emphasized the importance of faith and the belief in Jesus' authority to perform such miracles. The children listened intently, their eyes shining with wonder and amazement.

The little ones, inspired by Samuel's storytelling, approached life with a newfound understanding. They saw the world through lenses of faith, hope, and the belief in miracles. In their innocent hearts, they carried the knowledge that Jesus' power and authority extended beyond what they could comprehend.

Guided by the story of the miracle maker, the children aspired to share the love and compassion they had learned from Jesus' miracles. In their own unique ways, they became vessels of miracles themselves, bringing joy, healing, and hope to those in need.

The story of Samuel and the miracle maker spread throughout the village, inspiring others to recognize the power and love Jesus brought to the world. It remained a reminder of the miracles that occurred during Jesus' time and the enduring impact of his teachings.

And so, the story continued to be passed down from generation to generation, reminding children and adults alike of the immense power, love, and the authority behind Jesus' miracles. It served as a beacon of faith, teaching that the miracles of Jesus went beyond the pages of history, and that even today, one could witness and experience the transformative power of his love.

The shepherd care

In a small town nestled amidst rolling green meadows, there lived a young girl named Sarah. Sarah had a heart full of compassion and a deep love for animals. She spent her days exploring nature and observing the creatures that called it home. Each encounter with the animal kingdom filled her with awe and wonder.

One sunny day, as Sarah strolled through the town, she noticed a newly opened animal shelter. Her heart skipped a beat with excitement, and she couldn't resist stepping inside. The shelter was bustling with activity as volunteers fed, bathed, and comforted the furry residents.

Curiosity got the better of Sarah, and she approached the shelter's director to inquire about how she could contribute. The director, impressed by Sarah's passion, welcomed her with open arms, and Sarah became a dedicated volunteer at the shelter.

Through her volunteer work, Sarah experienced firsthand the joys and challenges of caring for the animals. She learned to feed them, clean their living spaces, and provide them with companionship and love. As she formed connections with the animals, Sarah discovered an unexpected parallel to the love and care that Jesus had for His flock.

Sarah noticed that just as she nurtured and protected the animals at the shelter, Jesus, the Good Shepherd, extended his love and protection to His people. She came to understand that she was imitating Jesus' care for the flock by tending to the animals with tenderness and selflessness.

Inspired by this realization, Sarah went above and beyond her duties at the shelter. She organized fundraising events, inviting the community to join her in supporting the welfare of the animals. Through her efforts, she raised awareness about responsible pet ownership and the importance of compassion towards all creatures.

As the shelter flourished under Sarah's care, the animals thrived, finding loving homes and experiencing the joy of being part of a family. The town took notice of Sarah's dedication and the positive impact she had made.

News of Sarah's efforts reached neighboring communities, inspiring others to follow in her footsteps. Animal shelters in surrounding towns witnessed an increase in volunteerism, fundraising, and pet adoptions as people recognized the significance of caring for God's creatures.

Sarah's story became an emblem of Jesus' love and care for His flock, reminding people of their responsibility to treat all living beings with love and compassion. The young girl's actions cultivated a sense of unity, empathy, and respect in the town and beyond.

Throughout her journey, Sarah never forgot the lessons she had learned about the parallel between caring for animals and Jesus' care for His people. She continued to advocate for the welfare of animals, spreading the message of love and compassion wherever she went.

And so, Sarah's story and her work at the animal shelter became an enduring tale of the Shepherd's care. It inspired generations to come, reminding them of their role in extending Jesus' love to all creatures, both great and small. Sarah's profound understanding of Jesus' care for His flock had transformed her heart, allowing her to be a beacon of compassion and kindness in a world that sorely needed it.

The Prodigal Son Returns

In a bustling city, there lived a family with two sons, Alex and Ethan, and their kind-hearted parents. The family worked hard and lived a comfortable life, but their prosperity often distracted them from the value of love and unity.

One fateful day, Ethan felt dissatisfied with his life and yearned for independence. He approached his father, requesting his inheritance early. The father, saddened by his son's desire to leave, reluctantly granted his request.

Ethan left the comforts of his family's home, eager to experience the allure of the city. For a time, he indulged in a lavish lifestyle, surrounded by so-called friends who only sought his wealth. The praise and attention he received at first seemed fulfilling, as he squandered all his inheritance on parties, material possessions, and selfish desires.

However, as time passed, Ethan's fortune began to dwindle. The supposed friends vanished, leaving him alone and destitute. Reality sank in, and Ethan found himself humbled and ashamed. He longed for the warmth and acceptance he had once taken for granted within his family.

With a heavy heart and a newfound humility, Ethan made the difficult decision to return home. He yearned for forgiveness and longed for the love he had forsaken.

Meanwhile, Alex, the faithful son, had stayed by his family's side, supporting and caring for his parents in their aging years. He watched as his younger brother embarked on his misguided journey, feeling a mixture of concern and sadness for the path he had chosen.

One afternoon, as Alex gazed out from his family's porch, he spotted a weary figure slowly approaching. He recognized the familiar silhouette of his brother immediately, and his heart filled with a mix of emotions.

Racing towards Ethan, Alex welcomed him home with open arms. He embraced his brother, tears streaming down his face, whispering, "I'm so glad you're back, Ethan. We've missed you."

Overwhelmed by his brother's unconditional love and forgiveness, Ethan found solace in Alex's warm embrace. He tearfully begged for forgiveness, confessing his sins and expressing deep remorse for the pain he had caused.

Their parents, hearing the commotion, rushed out to find their long-lost son standing before them. A mixture of emotions filled their hearts. Their love for Ethan had never ceased, and they greeted him with open arms, mirroring the faithful love of the father in Jesus' parable.

Together, the family celebrated Ethan's return. They prepared a feast, symbolizing forgiveness and the joyous reunion of a lost and found family member. In that moment, they understood the power of second chances and the depth of God's love and forgiveness.

The story of Ethan's prodigal journey and return spread throughout the city, touching the hearts of those who heard it. Children, teenagers, and adults alike learned the value of forgiveness and the unending love of God.

Through the modern-day adaptation of the prodigal son's story, children learned the importance of extending grace and forgiveness, even in the face of mistakes and regrets. They understood that no matter how far they may stray from God's path, His love and forgiveness would always be waiting, eager to embrace them upon their return.

As the city embraced the message of the prodigal son's return, forgiveness and second chances became woven into the fabric of their community. The story served as a reminder that God's love is boundless, and that no matter how far one may wander, the love of family and the forgiving embrace of God would always welcome them home.

The Fisherman's Faith

In a sleepy fishing village nestled along the shores of a tranquil sea, there lived a fisherman named Simon Peter. Simon Peter had spent countless nights casting his net into the water, hoping for a bountiful catch to support his family. However, the past few weeks had been filled with disappointment as the fish seemed to elude him.

One gloomy morning, Simon Peter set out on his boat. Weariness weighed heavy on his shoulders as doubts crept into his mind. "What's the use?" he muttered to himself. "I've been fishing all night, and there's nothing to show for it."

Just as Simon Peter was about to call it a day, a stranger approached. The stranger had kind eyes and a commanding presence. It was Jesus, the famed teacher and healer. Simon Peter had heard stories of Jesus' miracles and teachings, but little did he know that this encounter would change his life.

Jesus asked Simon Peter for permission to board the boat. Once on board, Jesus told Simon Peter to sail into deeper waters and cast his net. Though Simon Peter was fatigued and doubtful, he trusted the words of the wise teacher and followed his instructions.

As the net descended into the water, Simon Peter's heart was filled with both anticipation and skepticism. He suspected that this would be another failed attempt, but he obediently followed Jesus' command. Moments later, to his astonishment, the net began to strain, almost bursting with an overwhelming number of fish.

Simon Peter's doubt was washed away in an instant, replaced by awe and newfound faith. Trembling with excitement, he called to his fellow fishermen for help. Together, they hauled in the miraculous catch, their boat nearly sinking under the weight of the fish.

Falling to his knees at Jesus' feet, Simon Peter cried out, "Depart from me, for I am a sinful man, O Lord." But Jesus, with a gentle smile, reached out and touched Simon Peter's shoulder, saying, "Do not be afraid, Simon. From now on, you will fish for people."

Overwhelmed with a deep sense of reverence and understanding, Simon Peter accepted Jesus' call. He left behind his nets and followed Jesus, becoming one of His closest disciples. Through his unwavering faith and commitment, Simon Peter's life was forever transformed.

Simon Peter's miraculous catch became a testament to the power and authority of Jesus. The story spread throughout the village and beyond, igniting hope and faith in the hearts of those who heard it. People flocked to Jesus, eager to witness His miracles and learn from His teachings.

Simon Peter's doubts turned to unwavering faith as he witnessed the countless miracles Jesus performed. He witnessed the blind given sight, the sick healed, and the hungry fed. Through it all, Simon Peter became a pillar of strength within Jesus' ministry, sharing his own story of doubt and redemption.

This story of the fisherman's faith inspired generations to come. It showed them that faith, even in the face of doubt, could lead to miraculous outcomes. It taught them to trust in the guidance of Jesus, and to let go of skepticism when they were met with unexpected challenges.

And so, the tale of Simon Peter's faith spread far and wide, leaving an indelible mark on the hearts of all who heard it. It became a reminder that when we place our trust in Jesus, we can overcome the greatest doubts and witness the power of His love and grace in our lives.

The Golden Rule

In a bustling town named Harmonyville, two young friends named Matthew and Anna embarked on a remarkable journey rooted in the simple yet profound principle known as the Golden Rule. They were kind-hearted individuals who believed in treating others as they would like to be treated.

One sunny morning, as Matthew and Anna strolled through their neighborhood, they noticed a commotion near the local park. Curiosity drew them closer, and they saw a group of children engaged in a heated argument, their faces filled with frustration and hurt.

Moved by the distress on their peers' faces, Matthew and Anna decided to intervene. Remembering the importance of the Golden Rule, they approached the children with compassion and understanding. In their gentle voices, they encouraged both sides to listen to one another, to communicate their feelings, and to find common ground for resolution.

As the children followed Matthew and Anna's lead, an extraordinary transformation occurred. The heated arguments began to dissipate, replaced with open dialogue, empathy, and understanding. The children started treating one another with respect and kindness, using the Golden Rule as a guiding principle.

Inspired by the success of their intervention, Matthew and Anna realized that they could make a powerful impact by actively practicing the Golden Rule in their everyday lives. They made a pact to treat all individuals they encountered with the same respect and kindness they desired for themselves.

At school, Matthew listened attentively to his classmates, offering his support and encouragement. He recognized the importance of uplifting others, just as he himself desired to be uplifted. His classmates, touched by his genuine kindness, began to trust and confide in him, deepening their friendships.

Anna, on the other hand, took note of people's needs and sought ways to help. She held doors open, shared her belongings, and smiled at strangers. The ripple of kindness she created resonated within her community, fostering an environment where people felt valued and respected.

Matthew and Anna's example began to inspire others in Harmonyville. Individuals of all ages embraced the power of the Golden Rule, recognizing the transformational impact it had on their relationships. The town became a harmonious place, where the Golden Rule was practiced, and genuine connections flourished.

One day, as Matthew and Anna reflected on their journey, they marveled at how their commitment to the Golden Rule had spread love and unity throughout their community. The friends realized that the true impact of their actions extended far beyond themselves—it had touched the lives of countless others and forever shaped the fabric of Harmonyville.

Their dedication to treating others as they would like to be treated had created a loving and compassionate community. It had reminded them and others of the immense power of empathy and kindness. They understood that the Golden Rule was not merely a phrase; it was a way of life, a catalyst for positive change.

And so, Matthew, Anna, and the people of Harmonyville continued to live by the Golden Rule, cherishing their friendships, nurturing their relationships, and embracing the profound impact that treating others with love, respect, and kindness had on their community.

Together, they wrote a new chapter in the town's history—one woven with threads of compassion, unity, and enduring friendships. In Harmonyville, the Golden Rule was more than just a principle—it was a way of life that guided their actions, shaped their interactions, and fostered a community filled with love and understanding.

The Samaritan's compassion

In a bustling city filled with people hurrying to their destinations, a young girl named Emily stood out from the crowd. She had a heart brimming with compassion and a genuine desire to make a difference in the world. Emily always looked for opportunities to show kindness, just as her parents had taught her.

One sunny afternoon, as Emily walked through the city streets, she noticed a commotion around a street corner. Curiosity sparked within her, and she cautiously approached the scene. There, lying on the sidewalk, was a man in tattered clothes, looking weary and in pain.

Without hesitation, Emily knelt down beside the man and gently reached out a helping hand. She asked him if he was alright and if there was anything she could do to help. The man, deeply touched by her genuine concern, shared his story of struggle and loss.

Determined to alleviate his suffering, Emily immediately sprang into action. She purchased a meal from a nearby food stand, ensuring the man had something warm to eat. She then flagged down a passerby who had medical training, arranging for him to examine the man's injuries. Emily stayed by the man's side, providing comfort and support until help arrived.

In the midst of this act of compassion, a woman who had witnessed the scene approached Emily. Moved by her kindness, the woman introduced herself as Mrs. Anderson and offered her assistance. Emily gratefully accepted, knowing that together they could make an even greater impact.

With Mrs. Anderson's connections, they were able to secure a place for the man to receive proper care and shelter. They worked tirelessly to find resources and support to aid him in his journey to regain stability and rebuild his life.

News of Emily's selfless acts spread throughout the city, inspiring others to join in the mission of compassion and kindness. Individuals, inspired by

Emily's example, started mobilizing their efforts to help the less fortunate in their community.

Emily's story reached far and wide, reaching the hearts of countless individuals. People from different walks of life were encouraged by her genuine care for a stranger in need. They recognized the transformative power of love and compassion, realizing that it was through acts of kindness that they could create an inclusive and caring community.

Emily's parents, overwhelmed with pride, saw their daughter's impact and were inspired to join her mission. Together, as a family, they dedicated themselves to helping those in need, spreading the message of love and compassion wherever they went.

For Emily, the experience affirmed the importance of loving our neighbors as ourselves, irrespective of their background or circumstances. She learned that even the smallest act of kindness could make a profound difference in someone's life. Emily's compassion not only changed the life of the man she helped that day, but it also inspired an entire community to extend a helping hand to those in need.

And so, Emily's story became a reminder to all that compassion is a powerful force that can transform lives and bring hope to those who are suffering. Her example inspired others to look beyond themselves and to reach out with love and kindness, creating a world where everyone could thrive and experience the beauty of compassion.

The Power of Belief

In a village atop a majestic hill, a young boy named David lived amidst fields and sheep. David possessed a spirit of resilience and an unwavering faith in God. He would spend his days caring for his father's sheep, finding solace in the quiet moments of prayer and reflection.

One day, troubling news reached the village. A fearsome giant named Goliath had emerged, challenging the entire village to face him in battle. The villagers quivered with fear, for Goliath seemed invincible, his towering presence engulfing all who crossed his path.

David's heart burned with a passion to protect his people. Though he was young and untrained in the ways of war, he believed that with God on his side, no obstacle was insurmountable. Filled with faith, he volunteered to face Goliath, much to the astonishment of the villagers.

David approached the battlefront, armed not with physical might, but with a rock, a sling, and an unyielding belief in the power of God. As Goliath thundered his threats, David stood firm, proclaiming his faith and declaring that God would deliver him and his people from the giant's grasp.

Goliath, amused by the sight of a young boy facing him, mocked David's audacity. He advanced toward him, confident in his strength and superiority. However, David's trust in God was unshakeable.

With a single swing of his sling, David released the stone with precision. Time seemed to stand still as the rock found its mark, striking Goliath square in the forehead. The giant fell to the ground, defeated.

The villagers erupted in joyous celebration. The power of David's faith had triumphed, reminding them of the strength that could be found in unwavering belief. David's name echoed throughout the village, whispered in awe and reverence.

As David basked in the glory of his victory, he remained humble, giving full credit to God for the triumph. He knew that it was not his own strength but the power of his faith that had allowed him to overcome the seemingly insurmountable challenge.

News of David's remarkable feat spread to neighboring cities and towns. People far and wide were inspired by his story, grasping the significance of unwavering belief and the power of trusting in God. They recognized the possibility of conquering their own "giants" — the obstacles and challenges that loomed over their lives.

David's story became a source of hope, encouraging others to face their own giants with faith and courage. Throughout the generations, his example stood as a reminder that when one places their trust in God, no obstacle is too big to overcome.

As David continued his journey through life, he endeavored to live with the same faith and belief in God's power. He became a leader, guiding his people with wisdom and humility, always drawing upon the lessons he learned on the day he faced Goliath.

And so, the story of David and the giant Goliath echoed through the ages, inspiring generations to face their own challenges with a courageous and unwavering belief in the power of God. It stood as a testament to the extraordinary things that can be achieved when one places faith in a higher power and trusts in the strength that comes from within.

The Humble Sparrow

In the peaceful countryside, nestled amidst tall, swaying grasses and blooming wildflowers, there lived a small sparrow named Willow. Willow was a humble bird, blending into the tapestry of nature with her plain brown feathers and delicate chirp.

Every day, Willow watched as other birds soared gracefully through the sky, their vibrant colors and melodic songs capturing the attention of all who beheld them. She couldn't help but feel insignificant in comparison. "Why am I so plain?" she whispered to herself, as the wind whispered through the fields.

One sunny morning, as Willow perched on a gnarled branch, contemplating her existence, she noticed a group of children playing nearby. They laughed and ran, their eyes sparkling with joy. Willow observed them with curiosity, longing to understand the purpose she served in God's creation.

Intrigued, Willow began to follow the children on their adventures, keeping her distance so as not to frighten them. From a safe perch, she witnessed their compassion for injured creatures, their awe at the sight of delicate wildflowers, and their ability to find beauty in simple acts of kindness.

Days turned into weeks, and Willow's admiration for the children grew. Inspired by their pure hearts, she gradually understood that her seemingly plain appearance and soft song held a unique purpose in the grand tapestry of creation. She, too, could bring joy and teach valuable lessons through her humble existence.

One day, the children noticed Willow observing them from afar. They smiled at her and spoke words of encouragement. In their eyes, Willow saw the recognition of her worth. She realized that she brought them a special kind of joy, reminding them that even the smallest and seemingly insignificant creatures held value in God's eyes.

From that day forward, Willow embraced her role as the humble sparrow of the countryside. Through her gentle chirps and cheerful presence, she brought a sense of peace and harmony to all who encountered her. The children affectionately named her "Joyful Songbird" and celebrated her as a treasured part of God's creation.

News of Willow's impact spread throughout the village, inspiring others to appreciate and value the simplicity and beauty in nature. People began to notice the delicate wildflowers, the buzzing bees, and the gentle creatures that shared their world. They realized that every creature, no matter how small, played a vital role in God's grand design.

Willow's story touched the hearts of children and adults alike. At bedtime, parents would share her tale, teaching their children the importance of valuing every creature and recognizing the beauty in God's creation. The story of the humble sparrow became a reminder that no matter how insignificant one may seem, they hold a unique place and purpose in the world.

And so, Willow, the joyful and humble sparrow, continued to bring happiness and wisdom to those she encountered. From her place in the countryside, she echoed the message that every creature, no matter its size or appearance, was valuable in God's eyes. Her story taught children and adults that in the vastness of creation, the smallest and most unassuming beings had a meaningful part to play in the tapestry of life.

The Mystery of the Stolen Bible

In the quaint town of Harmonyville, four friends named Emma, Ethan, Lucas, and Olivia shared a deep love for adventure and solving mysteries. Their love for God's Word, the Bible, also bound them together as they recognized its significance in their lives.

One sunny afternoon, the friends gathered at their secret meeting spot, nestled beneath a grand oak tree. As they exchanged stories and laughter, an unsettling piece of news reached their ears: the local church's treasured Bible had been stolen. Shocked by this act of disrespect, they realized they had a mystery to solve.

Driven by their love for God's Word and determination to restore justice, the friends formed the Bible Detectives. With their magnifying glasses and notepads in hand, they dove into the investigation.

Their first stop was the church, where they questioned the pastor, the choir members, and churchgoers. The friends listened carefully, picking up clues and piecing the puzzle together. They discovered that the Bible had been urgently needed for a special ceremony and its loss deeply saddened the congregation.

With their list of suspects growing, the Bible Detectives set out to interview each person individually. As they dug deeper, they encountered unexpected twists and turns. The friends faced discouragement but leaned on their faith and the strength of their friendship. They reminded each other of the message within the stolen Bible and the impact it held for the entire community.

While searching for more leads, the friends stumbled upon a hidden passageway beneath the church. Intrigued, they followed the trail, led by flickering candlelight, until they reached a small, secret room. There, they discovered the stolen Bible tucked away, forgotten.

Overwhelmed with relief, the friends celebrated their victory. They returned the Bible to the church, where its rightful place was on the lectern, ready to spread God's Word throughout the community.

Through their adventure, the Bible Detectives learned an important lesson. They realized that the Bible was not just a book; it was a guide to life, filled with wisdom and love. Its words held the power to transform minds and hearts, providing strength, hope, and comfort.

Inspired by their experience, the friends started a Bible study group for children in the town. They gathered weekly, sharing stories from the Bible, discussing its lessons, and encouraging one another in their faith.

The impact of their detective work and their commitment to God's Word rippled throughout Harmonyville. Families began dusting off their own Bibles, rekindling their love for God's teachings. The stolen Bible mystery became a turning point, not only for the four friends but for the entire town.

The Bible Detectives, united by their adventure and newfound appreciation for God's Word, continued their mission of spreading its message throughout the town. They organized Bible studies, where children would gather to learn, discuss, and apply the valuable lessons found within its pages.

As the Bible Detectives nurtured their passion for God's Word, the children of Harmonyville began to experience its transformative power in their own lives. They discovered divine wisdom and guidance, enabling them to navigate challenges with grace and make decisions rooted in love and kindness.

The impact of the Bible Detectives' work reached far beyond their small town. News of their success and the ensuing spiritual revival traveled to neighboring communities. Inspired by the children's dedication, others formed their own detective groups, vowing to embark on their own missions to uncover the treasures hidden within the Bible.

With every passing day, the detectives witnessed the beautiful tapestry of faith unfolding in Harmonyville. Families carved out time for daily devotionals, spreading a spirit of unity and love within their households. The town became a place where the kindness of God's Word resonated through acts of compassion and understanding.

In their continued adventures, the Bible Detectives faced new challenges, sometimes encountering doubts and questions. However, they found solace in knowing that their faith in God's Word would guide them through any mystery or dilemma. They celebrated every discovery and embraced the lessons it brought, deepening their love for God and His teachings.

As years passed, the Bible Detectives grew older, ready to embark on their individual journeys beyond Harmonyville. They left behind a legacy of faith, hope, and the profound impact of God's Word in their lives and community.

However, the spirit of the Bible Detectives lived on. The children they had inspired carried their dedication to God's Word, cherishing its wisdom, and spreading its message throughout their respective corners of the world.

In Harmonyville, the stolen Bible mystery became a symbol of transformation. It served as a reminder of the endless possibilities that lie within God's Word and the importance of valuing and embracing its teachings. The town flourished as a place where God's love and truth thrived, igniting a flame of faith that would burn brightly for generations to come.

And so, the story of the Bible Detectives in Harmonyville became a testament to the power of God's Word and the profound impact it could have on individuals and communities. Their legacy served as an enduring reminder that discovering the truths within the Bible was a lifelong journey—one that would continue to shape and guide those who were willing to listen with open hearts and minds.

The Seeds of Faith

In a small, sunlit village, nestled among rolling hills, a young boy named Timmy lived with his family. Timmy adored spending time in his garden, where he learned about the wonders of nature and witnessed the growth of plants and flowers. One spring morning, as he held a handful of tiny seeds, Timmy's curiosity sparked an idea.

Eager to see the seeds transform into beautiful plants, Timmy began carefully planting them in the rich soil of his garden. He watered them, removed the weeds, and anxiously waited for signs of growth. As days turned into weeks, Timmy noticed a pattern - the seeds in some areas thrived, while others withered away.

Puzzled by this inconsistency, Timmy sought his grandfather's wisdom. His grandfather, a wise and gentle man, told him a story known as the parable of the sower from the Bible.

"Timmy," his grandfather began, "just like you plant seeds in your garden, there is a parable Jesus once told about a sower who went out to sow seeds. The seeds fell on different types of soil - the path, the rocks, the thorns, and the good soil. The ones that fell on fertile soil grew and produced a bountiful harvest, but the others struggled or were choked by the world."

Timmy listened intently, absorbing his grandfather's words. His grandfather continued, "The parable teaches us about faith and the condition of our hearts. When we receive God's Word and trust in Him with sincerity, our faith becomes like the seeds planted in good soil - it flourishes and bears much fruit. But we must be careful not to allow thorns, rocks, or distractions to hinder our faith."

Inspired by his grandfather's words, Timmy pondered the parable. He realized that faith, like a seed, needed the right environment to grow. He made a connection between his garden and the garden of his heart, understanding the significance of cultivating faith in God's Word.

Determined to nurture his faith, Timmy resolved to root out any thorns of doubt or distractions that could hinder its growth. He spent time reading the Bible and praying, opening his heart to God's love and guidance.

As Timmy cultivated his faith, he noticed a beautiful transformation within himself. His heart became filled with joy, peace, and a deep sense of purpose. He saw the world through the lens of God's love and felt a renewed sense of connection to those around him.

Timmy's newfound faith had a ripple effect, touching the lives of his family, friends, and even the community. His genuine kindness, compassion, and unwavering trust in God's Word became a shining light, inspiring others to explore their own faith and seek a deeper relationship with God.

One day, as Timmy walked through the village, he noticed a group of children playing near the old well. Curiosity led him to join them, and as they laughed and chatted, Timmy shared stories from the Bible, passing on the teachings and parables he had learned.

The children listened intently, captivated by Timmy's enthusiasm and passion for God's Word. They eagerly asked questions, and together they discovered its timeless wisdom and the relevance of its messages in their own lives.

Word of Timmy's gatherings spread throughout the village, and soon more children, youth, and even adults joined in these Bible study sessions. The community became alive with discussions, prayer, and a shared sense of faith.

Through their collective exploration of God's Word, the village grew stronger in faith and unity. The seeds of faith that Timmy had nurtured in his own heart had multiplied and taken root in the lives of those around him, birthing a vibrant community of believers.

As the years passed, Timmy's impact continued to flourish. He became a guiding light, encouraging others to embrace the power of faith and God's love. He shared lessons from the Bible with such warmth and relatability that people of all ages found comfort, wisdom, and reassurance in his words.

As an elderly man, Timmy looked back with gratitude at the journey his faith had taken him on. He marveled at the seeds of faith that he had planted and how they had blossomed, spreading God's love far and wide.

The garden of Timmy's heart overflowed with the fruits of faith - love, joy, peace, patience, kindness, goodness, faithfulness, gentleness, and self-control. These virtues radiated from him, touching every person he encountered, leaving a lasting impression on their lives.

Timmy's story became a timeless tale within the village, passed down through generations, reminding everyone of the importance of nurturing faith in God's Word. His legacy of planting seeds of faith and watching them grow reminded the villagers that faith was not meant to be hidden away but to be shared and passed on, illuminating the path for others to find a deeper connection with God.

And so, the community thrived in faith, filled with gratitude for the humble boy who had ignited the flame of faith within their hearts. Timmy's story became a testament to the significance of cultivating faith, and how even the smallest seeds, when nurtured with love, could grow into bountiful gardens, transforming lives and communities.

The Special Stained Glass

In the heart of a picturesque town, stood a magnificent old church, its stained glass windows reflecting colors like kaleidoscopes on sunny days. It was a place where people sought solace and inspiration, each window telling a unique story.

Olivia, a curious and observant girl, loved spending time in the church. One day, as she wandered through the sanctuary, she stumbled upon an old storeroom. Wreathed in shadows, it housed forgotten treasures of the church's past.

Guided by her intuition, Olivia stumbled upon a dusty, neglected stained glass window hidden behind a pile of old crates. Intrigued by its mysterious appearance, she carefully wiped away the grime and cobwebs, revealing a splendid scene depicting a radiant figure reaching towards a broken heart.

As Olivia traced the lines and admired the artistry, she noticed a small compartment hidden within the window frame. Trembling with anticipation, she opened it and found a parchment with a faded message that read, "Forgive and be forgiven."

Curiosity heightened, Olivia shared her discovery with the church's pastor, Reverend Thomas. Overwhelmed by the significance of the stained glass window, he explained its history – it depicted the story of forgiveness and redemption.

The window had been commissioned long ago to symbolize the power of forgiveness to heal broken hearts and reconcile relationships. However, over time, the message had been forgotten, lost in the midst of busyness and distractions.

Together, Olivia and Reverend Thomas dedicated themselves to bringing the hidden message of forgiveness back to the congregation. They organized workshops on forgiveness, encouraging people to let go of grudges and embrace the healing power of reconciliation.

The stories of forgiveness shared within the church's walls inspired a transformation within the community. Estranged family members mended broken relationships, friends who had drifted apart sought forgiveness and rekindled their bond, and community members resolved long-standing conflicts.

Olivia's discovery not only brought forgiveness to the forefront but also reminded people in the town of the importance of embracing redemption and extending grace. Through reflection and introspection, the congregation recognized that the power of forgiveness went beyond restoring broken relationships – it brought peace, healing, and personal growth.

As Olivia grew older, she carried the lessons of forgiveness and redemption with her. Inspired by the stained glass window, she became an advocate for healing and reconciliation wherever she went. Her life became an embodiment of the message she had discovered, a living testimony to the transformative power of forgiveness.

The special stained glass window became a cherished symbol within the church, reminding the congregation of the power of forgiveness to mend hearts and restore relationships. It served as a constant reminder that grace and redemption were available to all who sought them.

And so, the story of Olivia and the special stained glass window continued to inspire generations, fostering a community that understood the power of forgiveness and the healing that came with it. Through the window's message of forgiveness and redemption, hearts were forever changed, and the church thrived as a place of love, compassion, and healing.

The Talking Animals

In the heart of a lush and vibrant forest, a diverse group of animals coexisted, each going about their daily routines with minimal interaction. The squirrel scurried up trees, the rabbit hopped through meadows, and the birds sang a symphony from the treetops.

One fateful day, the forest was enveloped by a magical luminescence, as a shimmering rainbow light bathed the canopy. Startled, the animals gathered beneath the radiant glow, their eyes wide with curiosity.

To their astonishment, they discovered that they could now communicate with one another. The gift of speech had been granted to the creatures of the forest, enabling them to bridge the divide that had separated them for so long.

Excitement rippled through the animal community as they embarked on a journey of discovering each other's unique perspectives, skills, and needs. The rabbit conveyed the abundance of tasty grass in hidden clearings, while the squirrel shared the secrets of gathering and storing nuts for the winter.

The birds, with their aerial views, guided the others to hidden sources of water during the dry season. The mighty bear brought strength and protection, ensuring a safe space for everyone to thrive. The animals quickly realized that by relying on one another and working together, they could overcome the challenges of the forest and ensure the well-being of the entire community.

As they communicated and collaborated, unity flourished in the forest. The squirrel, the rabbit, the birds, and the bear forged deep bonds of friendship, embracing their individuality while recognizing the interdependence that made them stronger as a collective.

Their newfound understanding and teamwork became a catalyst for positive change. They realized that by combining their gifts and sharing their knowledge selflessly, they enhanced the harmony of the forest and fostered an environment where all creatures could thrive.

Together, they created a forest where animals supported each other in times of scarcity, celebrated each other's successes, and offered comfort in times of sorrow. They shared stories, wisdom, and laughter, becoming a tightly-knit community that lived in harmony and gratitude.

Word of the talking animals spread beyond the forest, reaching nearby communities and inspiring humans to reflect on the importance of unity and teamwork within their own lives. Families, friends, and neighbors adopted the spirit of cooperation and learned to appreciate the diverse talents and perspectives of those around them.

In the forest, the once-isolated animals flourished in their newfound unity, their unique voices blending together in a symphony of understanding and respect. The talking animals became beacons of cooperation, reminding all who encountered them of the power of collaboration and the beauty that emerges when individuals embrace their interconnectedness.

And so, the story of the talking animals in the forest became a timeless tale, encouraging children and adults alike to listen, communicate, and rely on one another, recognizing that unity and teamwork are the keys to creating a world where all creatures, human and animal alike, can thrive as one community.

The Gift of Generosity

In a bustling town, nestled among rolling hills and winding rivers, lived a young boy named Liam. Liam possessed a generous heart and a spirit of kindness. He had heard stories of Jesus' selflessness and the joy that came from giving, and he longed to experience that same joy in his own life.

One sunny day, as Liam walked through the town square, he noticed a commotion near a gathering of huts. Curiosity drew him closer, and he discovered a group of people in need. Their clothes were tattered, and their faces etched with exhaustion.

Moved by their plight, Liam's empathetic heart stirred within him. He realized that he had resources he could share - his extra clothing, books, and even food. Without hesitation, he approached the group and offered his help.

As Liam shared his possessions, a radiant light filled his soul. He experienced a profound happiness he had never known before. Seeing the gratitude in the eyes of those he helped, he understood that the joy of giving was even greater than he could have imagined.

Inspired by this, Liam continued to find opportunities to give. He volunteered at a local shelter, served meals to the hungry, and helped elderly neighbors with their chores. Each act of kindness deepened his understanding of the joy that came from selflessness.

Over time, the news of Liam's generosity spread throughout the town, and others were inspired to follow his example. Acts of kindness and giving became a common occurrence, weaving a beautiful tapestry of compassion and care that embraced the community.

One day, Liam encountered an older woman named Mrs. Jenkins, who had fallen on hard times. She was disheartened, having lost her job and struggling to make ends meet. Liam sensed her despair and offered a listening ear and support. He shared what he had learned about giving and the joy it brought into his life.

Moved by Liam's compassion, Mrs. Jenkins felt a spark of hope reignite within her heart. She realized that she too could make a difference in her own way. With Liam's encouragement, she reached out to others in need, forming a network of support and love within the community.

As time went on, Liam's acts of generosity and the ripple effect they had on others transformed the town. Generosity became deeply ingrained in the fabric of the community, binding its people together with a sense of unity and care. Liam's selflessness inspired a movement of kindness that touched the lives of everyone he encountered.

Through his acts of generosity, Liam experienced the joy that comes from following the example of Jesus. His selflessness radiated love and brought hope to those who needed it most. It taught him that giving not only benefits others but also nourishes the giver's spirit, bringing fulfillment and joy beyond measure.

And so, the story of Liam's gift of generosity continues to inspire generations, reminding all who hear it of the profound joy and impact that comes from selflessness. It serves as a reminder that by following in the footsteps of Jesus and opening our hearts to others, we can create a world where kindness and compassion abound, making a difference one generous act at a time.

The Miracle in the Garden

In a small suburban neighborhood, nestled at the end of the street, lived a girl named Hannah. Hannah had always been captivated by the beauty and wonder of nature. She often spent her afternoons tending to her garden, carefully planting seeds and nurturing them with love and care.

One spring morning, as Hannah stepped into her garden, she noticed a small sapling standing tall among her flowers. It seemed out of place, as if it had magically appeared overnight. Curiosity filled her heart as she examined the young tree's delicate leaves and slender branches.

Days turned into weeks, and Hannah witnessed an incredible transformation. The sapling grew rapidly, reaching towards the sky. It blossomed into a majestic tree with vibrant green leaves and branches extending far and wide, shading the rest of the garden with its canopy.

Amazed by the tree's rapid growth, Hannah marveled at this miracle in her garden. She knew it was a testament to God's incredible power of creation. She understood that just as God had fashioned the tree with precision and intricacy, He also had the power to shape her life and guide her journey.

One day, as Hannah admired the tree, she noticed an abundance of fruit hanging from its branches. The tree had become a source of provision, offering nourishment and sustenance. Overwhelmed with gratitude, Hannah realized that God's provision extended beyond just the physical world. He also provided for her emotional and spiritual needs, bringing joy, guidance, and love into her life.

Filled with a desire to share this miraculous experience, Hannah invited her friends and neighbors to witness the tree's transformation. They gathered beneath its shade, celebrating the beauty of nature and the power of God's provision. They marveled at how the tree had grown from a mere sapling into a sanctuary, providing shelter, beauty, and sustenance—a true gift from above.

News of the miracle in Hannah's garden spread throughout the neighborhood, inspiring others to reconnect with nature and recognize the awe-inspiring power of God's creation. People began spending more time outdoors, cultivating gardens, and appreciating the intricate designs of the natural world.

Hannah's garden became a place of solace and wonder, a reminder of the beauty and provision that God bestowed upon His creation. It served as a sanctuary where people gathered, shared stories, and found solace in the peaceful embrace of nature.

Years passed, and the tree in Hannah's garden continued to flourish, its branches reaching higher and wider. As Hannah grew older, she carried the lessons of the miracle in her garden with her. She recognized the importance of cultivating gratitude, trusting in God's provision, and cherishing the awe-inspiring power of His creation.

And so, the story of the miracle in Hannah's garden lived on—a testament to the undeniable power and beauty of God's creation and provision. It echoed through the neighborhood, inspiring others to cultivate their own gardens of gratitude, trust, and awe, and reminding all who heard it of the miracles that surround us every day, waiting to be discovered with grateful hearts.

The Courageous Esther

In a kingdom nestled among rolling hills, there lived a courageous and wise young girl named Esther. She possessed a heart full of compassion and a spirit of bravery. Esther lived in a time when her people faced great adversity, and their very existence was under threat.

Amidst this turmoil, a powerful ruler named King Xerxes ruled over the land. His advisor, the wicked Haman, devised a plot to harm Esther's people, the Jews. Unaware of Esther's true identity as a Jew, she was chosen to be part of the king's harem.

Esther's uncle, Mordecai, urged her to reveal her true identity and approach the king, imploring him to spare their people. Esther knew the dangers that awaited her—a breach of protocol could lead to her own demise. However, she found strength in her faith and believed that God had placed her in this position for a reason.

With the weight of determination upon her shoulders, Esther fasted and prayed, seeking divine guidance and courage. When the time was right, she approached the throne of King Xerxes, relying on her faith to guide her every step.

As Esther stood before the king, her courage shone bright, illuminated by her unwavering trust in God. With grace and poise, she revealed her true identity and pleaded for the lives of her people.

King Xerxes, moved by Esther's bravery and wisdom, listened attentively. He recognized the injustice that had been planned against the Jews and vowed to protect them, ensuring Haman faced the consequences of his wicked plot.

Esther's faith and bravery saved her people from harm, and the Jewish community celebrated their deliverance. They rejoiced, recognizing Esther as a true hero—a beacon of hope and a living testament to God's providence.

The story of Esther's courage and faith spread far and wide, inspiring generations to come. Children admired her bravery and strength, learning the importance of standing up for what is right, even in the face of adversity. Esther's story reminded them of the power of faith, prayer, and trusting in God's guidance.

From that moment forward, Esther's name became synonymous with courage, and her story was shared among families and communities. Children and adults alike drew inspiration from her unwavering faith and her willingness to risk everything for the sake of others.

Esther's legacy lived on, reminding everyone that even in the most challenging of circumstances, God can use ordinary individuals to accomplish extraordinary things. Her story encouraged people to stand up against injustice, fight for their beliefs, and trust in God's provision.

And so, the courageous Esther continued to inspire generations, teaching children and adults alike the importance of bravery, faith, and the remarkable power of trusting in God's plan. Her name became synonymous with strength and resilience, a reminder that with faith and courage, anyone can make a difference in the world.

The Healing Tears

In a cozy town nestled by a glistening lake, a young girl named Grace possessed a heart overflowing with empathy and compassion. Her warm smile radiated kindness, and her gentle presence brought comfort to those around her.

One sunny afternoon, while sitting by the lakeside, Grace received grave news—her dear friend Sarah had fallen ill. Determined to bring comfort and healing to her friend's side, Grace hurriedly made her way to Sarah's home.

As Grace entered Sarah's room, she discovered her friend lying weakly in bed. Sarah's face, once vibrant, was now etched with pain and worry. Grace approached her gently and held her hand, silently communicating a world of love and support.

With tears welling in her eyes, Grace whispered, "Sarah, I am here for you. You are not alone in this journey." Her heartfelt words brought a flicker of hope to Sarah's weary eyes.

Days turned into weeks, and Grace remained faithfully by Sarah's side. She listened as Sarah expressed her fears, offering words of encouragement and soothing presence. Grace brought small gifts—a favorite book, a bouquet of wildflowers—to brighten Sarah's room and remind her of the beauty that still surrounded them.

One evening, as Grace sat beside Sarah, tears welled in her eyes. In that moment, something remarkable happened—the air around them seemed to change, as if filled with a healing presence. A single tear escaped Grace's eye and touched Sarah's cheek, transmitting a wave of comfort and warmth.

To their astonishment, Sarah's pain eased, and a sense of peace washed over her. Grace realized that her own tears, shed out of empathy and compassion, held a unique healing power that touched the depths of Sarah's soul.

Word of this miraculous encounter spread throughout the town, capturing the hearts of those who heard the tale. People came to Grace seeking solace and healing, drawn to her remarkable ability to bring comfort through her tears.

As time passed, Grace became known as "the girl with healing tears." She embraced her unique gift, offering solace to those in need. Her compassion and empathy touched the lives of many, bringing healing and hope to those facing physical or emotional pain.

But to Grace, the true power of her tears lay in their ability to open hearts and foster authentic connections. Supported by her faith and guided by love, her tears encouraged others to embrace empathy and compassion, fostering a community where everyone felt seen, heard, and loved.

And so, Grace's story of healing tears continued, spreading a message of empathy and compassion throughout the town. It became a reminder that in times of difficulty, a simple act of love and understanding could bring immense comfort and healing. Inspired by Grace, the community learned the power of embracing emotions and offering presence and empathy to one another, creating a world where tears were not seen as weakness, but as a testament to the profound connection we share as human beings.

The Lost Key

In a charming village nestled between rolling hills, a young boy named Jack possessed an insatiable curiosity. His wide eyes and adventurous spirit often led him on quests to uncover hidden wonders within the town.

One sunny afternoon, while exploring an old attic, Jack stumbled upon a dusty, ancient key tucked away in the corner. Intrigued by its mystery, Jack held the key to the light and noticed an inscription engraved upon it: "Seek first the kingdom of God and His righteousness."

Puzzled yet excited, Jack embarked on a journey to decipher the meaning behind these words. He visited the wise old librarian, Mrs. Thompson, who shared stories of ancient legends and the power of faith. She explained that seeking God's kingdom and righteousness meant living a life aligned with His values and teachings.

Filled with a newfound purpose, Jack set off on a quest to discover what treasures seeking God's kingdom and righteousness could bring. He knew it would require seeking wisdom, showing kindness, and following God's commandments.

As Jack embarked on his journey of seeking, he experienced moments of doubt and challenges. However, with each obstacle, he held fast to his faith and remembered the inscription on the key. He discovered that seeking God's kingdom and righteousness meant seeking justice, showing compassion, and spreading love—values that elevated his spirit and brought Him closer to God.

During his adventure, Jack encountered diverse individuals who shared their stories of seeking God's kingdom and righteousness. A humble baker spoke of finding purpose in providing nourishment and kindness to others. A wise old gardener revealed how cultivating beauty in the world mirrored God's creation.

One day, as Jack explored an ancient forest, he stumbled upon a hidden door. With anticipation and a trembling hand, he inserted the key into the lock. As the door creaked open, a vast treasure awaited him—a treasure not of gold or jewels, but of peace, joy, and an unwavering connection to God.

This treasure filled Jack's heart, affirming the value of seeking God's kingdom and righteousness. He realized that true richness lay in aligning his life with God's will, nurturing his relationship with Him, and following His teachings.

From that day forward, Jack's perspective shifted. He no longer sought worldly treasures or fleeting pleasures, but instead focused on seeking God's kingdom and righteousness. He embraced a life of integrity, compassion, and love, becoming a beacon of light in his community.

Word of Jack's transformation and the lesson of seeking God's kingdom and righteousness spread throughout the village. The townsfolk, inspired by his example, embarked on their own journeys of seeking, experiencing the profound blessings and treasures that came from aligning their lives with God's purpose.

And so, Jack's discovery of the lost key became a catalyst for transformation and a living example of the value of seeking God's kingdom and righteousness. His journey taught him that true treasure lies not in what the world deems valuable but in the richness of a purposeful life lived in alignment with God's will.

The Wise Builder

In a small town surrounded by rolling hills, a curious and eager young boy named Charlie lived with his loving family. Charlie possessed a deep yearning for knowledge and a desire to understand profound truths.

One sunny day, as Charlie walked through the town square, he noticed a crowd gathered near the local temple. Intrigued, he joined them and listened attentively as a wise teacher shared a parable about a wise builder.

The teacher spoke about two builders—one who built his house upon a sturdy foundation of rock, and the other who built upon shifting sand. The first builder's house stood firm even in the face of storms, while the second builder's house crumbled under the force of the elements.

This parable resonated deeply within Charlie's heart. He understood that the house represented his faith, and the foundation was what he built his faith upon. Determined to apply this lesson to his own life, Charlie sought to understand the strong foundation he needed for his faith.

Driven by a desire for wisdom, Charlie sought out the teacher after the crowds dispersed. "How do I build my faith upon a strong foundation?" Charlie asked with sincere earnestness.

The wise teacher smiled warmly and replied, "Building a strong foundation for your faith involves listening to the teachings of Jesus and living by His words. His teachings are like the solid rock upon which you can build your faith. They provide guidance, hope, and strength."

Inspired by the teacher's words, Charlie eagerly dove into the teachings of Jesus. He read the stories of love, compassion, forgiveness, and wisdom. He discovered the importance of prayer, gratitude, and serving others selflessly.

As Charlie lived according to these teachings, he noticed a transformation within himself. His faith grew stronger, and he felt a profound sense of peace and contentment. Through trials and challenges, Charlie found solace in the unwavering foundation of his faith—a foundation rooted in Jesus' teachings.

With this newfound understanding, Charlie embraced a life built on the strong foundation of Jesus' teachings. He shared his knowledge with family and friends, spreading the wisdom and love he had gained.

The impact of Charlie's transformed faith reverberated throughout the town. Friends, neighbors, and strangers alike witnessed the joy and peace radiating from Charlie's spirit. Intrigued by the source of his strength, they too sought to build their faith upon the solid foundation of Jesus' teachings.

As the years passed, Charlie remained a beacon of light and wisdom in the town. His unwavering faith and firm foundation inspired countless others to seek Jesus and build their lives upon His teachings. Through his example, Charlie awakened a community to the transformative power of faith rooted in Jesus Christ.

And so, the story of Charlie, the wise builder, continued to touch the hearts and souls of those who heard it. It reminded them of the importance of building their faith on the strong foundation of Jesus' teachings—a foundation that could withstand any storm and bring immeasurable joy, peace, and strength.

The Secret Prayer Warriors

In a small town nestled among rolling meadows and glistening streams, a group of friends named Emma, Michael, Sarah, and Lucas found themselves drawn together by a common desire—to deepen their connection with God and experience the power of prayer.

One tranquil afternoon, as they gathered by the old oak tree in their favorite spot, inspiration struck like a gentle breeze. They agreed to form a secret prayer group, calling themselves the Prayer Warriors.

The Prayer Warriors met regularly, seeking solace and strength in prayer. They shared their joys and concerns, lifting each other up with fervent supplication. Their bond grew stronger as they realized the incredible support and comfort that came from heartfelt prayer.

At school, Emma's friend Michelle faced a challenging situation. She felt lost and unsure of what to do. The Prayer Warriors rallied together, offering their prayers and support for Michelle. In the days that followed, they witnessed a remarkable transformation as Michelle found guidance and peace, ultimately making the right choices.

News of the Prayer Warriors' impact spread like wildfire through the town. Families facing illness sought their prayers for healing. Local businesses asked for prayers for prosperity and harmony. People of all walks of life felt drawn to the warmth and compassion emanating from this group of friends.

One day, as the Prayer Warriors gathered near the town square, they noticed a weariness in the eyes of the townspeople—a collective burden that seemed overwhelming. The Prayer Warriors resolved to step out of their secret comfort zone and extend their prayers to the community at large.

They organized a prayer gathering open to all, inviting everyone to join in lifting up their hopes, concerns, and aspirations to God. The townspeople poured into the square, forming a circle of unity and faith. Prayers soared heavenward, creating a sacred bond that transcended individual struggles and embraced the collective wellbeing of the community.

In the days and weeks that followed, the town experienced a newfound spirit of hope and resilience. Answers to prayers manifested in unexpected ways—broken relationships healed, families reunited, and dreams breathed to life. The town's once-weary hearts found solace and strength through the power of unified prayer.

The Prayer Warriors realized the incredible impact their simple act of coming together had on the community. They witnessed countless testimonies of transformed lives, renewed spirits, and inspiring acts of kindness. Their secret prayer group blossomed into a powerful force of love and intercession, bringing restoration and hope to all they encountered.

From that day forward, the Prayer Warriors continued their mission of praying for their community. Prayer gatherings became a regular occurrence, and their secret prayer group became a source of inspiration for others to form prayer circles in their neighborhoods and workplaces.

The story of the Secret Prayer Warriors spread far beyond the town, touching the lives of countless people and inspiring them to seek the incredible power of prayer. Hearts around the world were united in faith, recognizing that in the presence of God, through the power of prayer, miracles could unfold, guiding communities toward healing and harmony.

And so, the story of the Secret Prayer Warriors lived on—a timeless reminder of the extraordinary power of prayer and the beautiful unity that emerges when people come together in faith, lifting each other up and seeking the presence of a loving God.

The Light in Darkness

In a world cloaked in darkness, both literally and metaphorically, there lived a young girl named Evelyn. Born with an extraordinary gift, Evelyn possessed a radiant light within her soul. Her mere presence brought warmth and comfort to those around her.

Evelyn understood the struggles faced by the world. She knew that fear, despair, and uncertainty shrouded the hearts of many. Determined to make a difference, she embarked on a mission to be a light amidst the darkness.

With a lantern in hand, Evelyn ventured into the darkest corners, both physical and emotional, where hope seemed distant. She knew that her light had the power to dispel fear, ignite hope, and guide others on a path towards healing.

In the shadowed alleyways of the city, Evelyn's lantern cut through the gloom, revealing a path to safety for those lost and afraid. She listened to their stories, offering a comforting presence and gentle words of encouragement. Her light symbolized a beacon of hope, showing that even in the darkest times, there is a way forward.

But Evelyn's mission went beyond illuminating the physical darkness. She ventured into the depths of emotional despair, reaching out to those burdened by pain and grief. Her light, a metaphor for her empathy and compassion, shone brightly as she held space for their sorrows, providing solace and reminding them that they were not alone.

Word of Evelyn's radiant light spread far and wide. People sought her out, drawn to her compassionate heart and the hope she exuded. Many who had lost their way rediscovered their strength and purpose through the light she shared.

But Evelyn knew that her light was not her own. It was a reflection of a greater source—the source of all goodness and love. Her light served as a reminder to all that there was a divine presence within each person, waiting to be embraced and shared with the world.

As Evelyn continued her journey, she encountered others who carried their own lights. Together, they formed a network of light-bearers, illuminating the world with compassion and kindness. Their collective glow transformed communities and inspired change, bringing forth solutions in the face of challenges and fostering unity among diverse individuals.

Evelyn's path was not without difficulties. She encountered skeptics and doubters, those who believed that darkness was insurmountable. But Evelyn persevered, unwavering in her conviction that even the smallest light can make a profound difference.

As years turned into decades, Evelyn's light continued to shine, guiding and uplifting all who crossed her path. Her legacy lived on, reminding generations that in times of darkness, there are ordinary people with extraordinary hearts who can be a beacon of hope and love.

And so, the story of Evelyn, the light-bearer, resonated through the ages. It served as a timeless reminder of the power of compassion, kindness, and being a source of light for others. Through her example, people learned that even amidst the deepest darkness, a single light can illuminate the way, inviting others to walk alongside and create a brighter, more hopeful world.

The Great Adventure

In a cozy little town, nestled at the foot of majestic mountains, there lived three adventurous siblings named Emily, Joshua, and Olivia. One day, while rummaging through their grandparents' attic, they stumbled upon an old, weathered map tucked away in a dusty chest.

Their eyes sparkled with excitement as they unfolded the map, revealing a mysterious trail leading to a hidden treasure. They knew that they had to embark on the great adventure that awaited them.

Under the warm glow of the morning sun, the siblings set off, their hearts filled with anticipation. As they followed the map's clues, they encountered challenges, obstacles, and moments of doubt. But they held onto their faith in God's guidance and trusted that He would lead them safely to the treasure.

Their journey took them through dense forests, across treacherous rivers, and up steep cliffs. But with each step, their bond grew stronger, and their trust in God deepened. They learned to rely on each other's strengths and to support one another in times of need.

Along the way, they encountered kind strangers who offered them food and shelter, reminding the siblings of God's provision and the kindness of His people. These encounters reiterated the lesson that God places individuals in their lives to help and guide them on their journey.

As they neared the final destination marked on the map, their excitement intensified. They stood before a towering waterfall, its mist glistening under the sun's rays. As they closely examined the waterfall, they discovered a hidden cavern behind it, concealing the long-lost treasure.

But much to their surprise, the treasure was not what they had expected. Instead of jewels and gold, it was a chest filled with priceless artifacts that spoke of wisdom, love, and faith. It contained ancient scrolls, inscribed with stories of God's faithfulness throughout history.

In that moment, the three siblings understood the true treasure they had found. It was not material wealth, but the knowledge that God had been their guiding light throughout the entire adventure. They had grown in faith, trust, and unity as they followed His lead, learning valuable lessons along the way.

With hearts full of gratitude, the siblings made their way back home, carrying the treasure of faith and a renewed sense of purpose. They shared their story with family and friends, inspiring others to embark on their own adventure of faith, trusting in God's guidance.

And so, the story of the great adventure lived on in the hearts of the siblings and those they encountered. It served as a testament to the power of trust in God's guidance, the importance of unity within a family, and the incredible treasures that await those who embark on a journey of faith.

The Garden of Gratitude

In a peaceful town surrounded by blooming gardens, a young girl named Emily had a heart filled with gratitude. She believed that even the smallest blessings in life deserved acknowledgment and appreciation.

Inspired by her love for nature and gratitude, Emily decided to create a special gratitude garden. With her small gardening tools in hand, she began tending to a patch of earth in her backyard.

Emily carefully planted seeds for flowers known for their beauty and uplifting scents. Every day, she watered the soil, pulling weeds, and nurturing each delicate plant. As the garden grew, so did her gratitude for God's blessings.

In her garden, Emily placed a small stone engraved with the word "gratitude" as a reminder of her purpose. She dedicated herself to gardening with gratefulness, choosing to see the beauty in every aspect of life.

Each morning, Emily spent time in her gratitude garden, expressing thanks for the gift of a new day. She thanked God for the warmth of the sun, the sweet fragrance of the flowers, the clean air she breathed, and the joy of being alive.

As she tended to her garden, Emily realized that cultivating gratitude in her heart was like nurturing the plants. It required attentiveness, patience, and a deep appreciation for the blessings that surrounded her.

Word of Emily's gratitude garden spread throughout the town, inspiring others to nurture their own gratitude and recognize the simple joys in life. Families and friends began setting aside time to express gratitude and thankfulness for the loved ones, experiences, and blessings that enriched their lives.

Emily's garden became a gathering place, where loved ones would sit among the blossoms, sharing stories and cherishing the beauty of gratitude. The garden created a space for reflection, where people were uplifted and reminded of God's goodness.

With time, Emily's garden flourished, inviting butterflies to dance among the flowers and birds to sing in delight. Her heart also blossomed with sincere gratitude, and she inspired many others to cultivate a similar spirit of thankfulness.

As Emily grew older, she continued to tend to her gratitude garden, sharing its lessons with new generations. Her dedication to gratitude became a lasting legacy, reminding people to cultivate gratefulness in their hearts and find joy in the everyday blessings that God had bestowed upon them.

And so, the story of Emily and her gratitude garden lived on as a testament to the power of cultivating gratitude. It encouraged people to pause, reflect, and appreciate the simple wonders of life. The garden stood as a symbol of the beauty that emerges when hearts are filled with thankfulness, reminding all who beheld it of the abundance of God's blessings.

The Helping Hands

In the heart of a vibrant town, a group of friends named Anna, Ben, Claire, and David felt inspired to make a difference in their community. They believed that even small acts of kindness could create a ripple effect, spreading joy and making a meaningful impact on the lives of others.

Under the shade of a grand oak tree, they gathered and formed a club called "The Helping Hands." Their mission was clear: to serve their community with selflessness and compassion. Together, they brainstormed creative ways to bring joy and assistance to those in need.

Their first project was to organize a food drive. The Helping Hands set up bins in local grocery stores and went door-to-door, collecting donations for the town's food pantry. They were overjoyed with the overwhelming response of support from their community.

Spurred on by their initial success, The Helping Hands ambitiously sought new ways to serve. They organized neighborhood clean-up events, helping to beautify public spaces. They volunteered at the local hospital, visiting patients and offering them comfort and companionship during their stay.

One day, they met an elderly couple, Mr. and Mrs. Smith, who lived alone and struggled with maintaining their garden. The Helping Hands sprang into action, weeding, planting, and transforming the neglected space into a colorful oasis. Mr. and Mrs. Smith were overwhelmed with gratitude, and the joy in their eyes warmed the hearts of The Helping Hands.

With each act of selflessness, the bond among The Helping Hands grew stronger. They realized that their purpose went beyond serving others—it was about cultivating a spirit of generosity and becoming the change they wished to see in the world.

News of The Helping Hands' efforts spread throughout the town, inspiring others to embrace kindness and take action. Students, families, and local businesses joined the movement, forming a web of community support that embraced the power of serving others.

As years passed, The Helping Hands became an integral part of the town's fabric, bringing joy, hope, and practical assistance to those in need. With each act of selflessness, they discovered a deeper sense of fulfillment and the joy that comes from being a channel of love and compassion.

The Helping Hands taught their community the value of lending a hand, no matter how small the act may seem. They showed that a single act of kindness had the power to brighten someone's day, restore faith, and transform lives.

And so, the story of The Helping Hands lived on, inspiring generations to come. It reminded people that each person has the ability to make a positive impact, to be a light in someone's darkness, and to work together in creating a more caring and compassionate world.

As The Helping Hands continued their journey of selflessness, they found that the true reward lay not just in the gratitude they received but in the joy that radiated within their own hearts. They discovered that it is in serving others that they found their own purpose and experienced the true beauty of what it means to be human.

The Musical Gift

In a small village nestled among rolling hills, there lived a shy and introverted child named Lily. Lily possessed a natural gift for music, but her fear of attention held her back from sharing it with the world. However, deep within her heart, a melody yearned to be set free.

One sunny day, while wandering through the village, Lily stumbled upon an old, abandoned piano in a dusty corner of the town square. Drawn to it, she hesitantly sat on the stool and gently pressed her fingers against the keys. A beautiful sound filled the air, and in that moment, Lily realized the power of her musical gift.

Encouraged by this newfound discovery, Lily timidly shared her compositions with her parents. They were in awe of her talent and encouraged her to use her gift to worship and praise God. Lily, inspired by their words, decided to step out of her comfort zone and use her music as a means to spread joy and praise.

With her heart full of determination, Lily joined the village church choir. Standing in the midst of her fellow choir members, she allowed her voice to blend harmoniously with others, celebrating the beauty of communal worship. Her gentle melodies enchanted the congregation, who joyfully lifted their voices in response.

As Lily gained confidence, she began to share her musical gift beyond the church walls. She performed at local community events, nursing homes, and parks. Her music brought smiles to faces, prompting hearts to overflow with gratitude.

Word of Lily's musical gift spread throughout the village and beyond. Soon, she received invitations to perform at prestigious events, sharing her talent on grand stages. Audiences marveled at the depth of emotion and the pure joy that emanated from her music.

Yet, amidst the newfound fame and acclaim, Lily remained grounded. She knew that her gift was not merely for her own glory but to honor and worship God. Each note she played or sang was an offering of praise, a way to share the love and beauty she had experienced within her heart.

Lily's music continued to touch lives and inspire people of diverse backgrounds. Her melodies carried messages of hope, encouragement, and faith, reminding listeners of the goodness and love of God.

As years passed, Lily's musical gift continued to flourish, echoing through generations. She mentored aspiring musicians, encouraging them to use their talent for the glory of God. Lily humbly acknowledged that her gift was bestowed upon her for a divine purpose and that it was her responsibility to nurture it and share it with others.

And so, the story of Lily and her musical gift echoed through the years, inspiring people to step out in faith, overcome their fears, and share their unique talents with the world. Lily's legacy reminded all who heard her music that the beauty of artistic expression was a divine gift meant to uplift, inspire, and bring joy.

The Kindness Cookies

In a bustling town filled with bustling streets, a young girl named Maya found solace in the sweet art of baking. She possessed a unique talent for creating delicious treats that brought smiles to the faces of all who tasted them. Maya's heart overflowed with love and compassion, and she believed that even a small act of kindness could make a big difference in someone's life.

One day, as Maya walked through the town square, she noticed a woman sitting on a bench, her face filled with sadness. Maya approached her, offering a warm smile and a freshly baked cookie. The woman's eyes sparkled with surprise and gratitude as she bit into the cookie, savoring the sweet flavors. Maya's simple act of kindness brought a flicker of light to the woman's day, reminding her that she was not alone.

Inspired by the connection she had made, Maya decided to take her acts of kindness to the next level. She decided to bake cookies with a purpose. Maya called them "Kindness Cookies." Each cookie was filled with love, compassion, and a message of hope. She packaged them beautifully and set out on a mission to spread kindness throughout the town.

Maya started by visiting the local hospital, delivering her Kindness Cookies to patients and nurses. Their faces lit up with delight, and for a moment, their worries seemed to fade away as they savored the sweetness of Maya's creations. Maya's cookies became a source of comfort and joy in times of difficulty.

Word quickly spread about Maya's Kindness Cookies, and soon people from all walks of life sought her out. She delivered batches of cookies to orphanages, homeless shelters, and nursing homes, bringing light and delight to those in need. Each interaction filled Maya's heart with a sense of purpose and fulfillment.

As her acts of kindness multiplied, a sense of unity and compassion spread throughout the town. People began to pay Maya's kindness forward, performing their own acts of compassion and spreading love in their own unique ways. The ripple effect of Maya's small acts of kindness transformed the community into a tapestry woven with threads of compassion and empathy.

Years passed, and Maya's Kindness Cookies became legendary. Her legacy lived on in the hearts of those who had received her cookies and witnessed the power of small acts of compassion. The town had become a place where kindness reigned, making it a little brighter and a little sweeter.

Maya's story inspired generations to carry on the torch of kindness and compassion. As Maya grew older, she trained aspiring bakers in the art of making Kindness Cookies, passing on her recipes and the importance of spreading love through small acts of compassion.

The tradition of the Kindness Cookies continued to flourish, extending its reach to neighboring towns and cities. Maya's legacy transcended generations, inspiring countless individuals to embrace kindness as a way of life. It became a symbol of the town's identity, attracting visitors who marveled at the warmth and love that radiated from its people.

To honor Maya's incredible contributions, the community organized an annual Kindness Festival—a celebration dedicated to acts of compassion and spreading joy. Families, friends, and strangers came together to bake and distribute Kindness Cookies, creating a wave of love that permeated every street corner.

As the festival grew, so did the impact of the Kindness Cookies movement. People fondly shared stories of how a simple bite into a cookie had brought them comfort during difficult times. The power of Maya's small acts of compassion became a beacon of hope and an inspiration for others to make a difference in their own unique ways.

Maya, in her later years, witnessed the exponential growth of kindness she had ignited. With a heart full of gratitude, she realized that love truly knows no bounds. From that point forward, she focused her energy on mentoring young bakers, helping them create their own recipes of kindness and showcasing their talents through the Kindness Cookies initiative.

As Maya passed her mantle to the next generation of bakers, the town's spirit of compassion continued to flourish. The Kindness Festival became an annual tradition celebrated throughout the region, fostering a culture of love, empathy, and selflessness.

Maya's impact extended beyond the town's borders, capturing the attention of organizations devoted to promoting kindness and humanitarian efforts. Maya's Kindness Cookies initiative gained recognition far and wide, inspiring similar projects in communities around the world.

Maya's legacy will forever live on, a testament to the incredible power of small acts of compassion. Her humble baking talent, coupled with her compassionate heart, transformed lives, built bridges, and reminded people of the goodness that resides within each of us.

And so, the story of the Kindness Cookies continues to inspire and remind us that even a small gesture of love can make an immeasurable difference in someone's life. As long as there are people like Maya, who choose kindness as their compass, the world will continue to be a place where love and compassion can prevail.

The Peaceful Pond

In a tranquil corner of the countryside, nestled amidst a lush green meadow, there lay a peaceful pond. In this idyllic oasis, a family of ducks—Mr. and Mrs. Mallard and their three ducklings, Lily, Oliver, and Emily—resided, delighting in the serene beauty that surrounded them.

As the five ducks went about their daily lives, they encountered numerous challenges, both big and small. Fierce storms would arrive, disrupting their peaceful routines. Food became scarce during particularly dry seasons, testing their endurance. Yet, amidst these trials, the family of ducks learned to lean on their unwavering trust in God, finding solace in His providence.

One stormy evening, as dark clouds blanketed the sky, heavy rain poured down upon the meadow. The once calm pond grew turbulent, and the little ducklings anxiously huddled together under the shelter of their parents' wings. In the face of the tempest, they found solace in their trust in God, surrendering to His power and knowing that He would guide them through the storm.

Days turned into weeks, and the ducks faced another challenge—the scarcity of food caused by a prolonged drought. The once bountiful meadow became barren, and the ducks felt the pangs of hunger. However, their parents, Mr. and Mrs. Mallard, taught them to trust in God's provision, reminding the little ones of the countless times their needs had already been met.

Just as the ducks reached a point of despair, a gentle rain began to fall, breaking the drought. New life sprouted from the once parched earth, and the meadow burst forth in vibrant greenery. The family of ducks feasted on new plants and insects, their hunger satisfied, and their faith in God's providence reaffirmed.

Through these trials, the ducks learned that surrendering to God's plan brought them an inexplicable peace. They discovered that even during the darkest storms and most challenging times, there was a greater purpose and a divine order at work, guiding their path.

As the ducklings grew and prepared to fly off on their own, they held fast to the lessons their parents had taught them. They ventured beyond the peaceful pond, encountering new hardships and joys along their individual journeys. Each step reinforced their parents' teachings—to surrender to God's plan, trust His guidance, and find peace in His providence.

Years passed, and the family of ducks reunited at the peaceful pond, older and wiser. They realized that life's challenges had molded them into resilient creatures of faith. They shared stories of their individual adventures, celebrating the moments where God's hand had guided them through trials and provided unexpected blessings.

As the sun set over the tranquil pond, the ducks marveled at the beauty surrounding them. They knew that even though the path ahead would be filled with uncertainty, their faith and trust in God's providence would remain unshakable.

And so, the story of the peaceful pond and the family of ducks serves as a timeless reminder of the peace that comes from surrendering one's worries and fears to God. It teaches us to trust in His plan, knowing that He works with love and wisdom, guiding us through the storms and leading us to the paths of peace and purpose.

The Humble Servant

In a vibrant neighborhood, a young girl named Lily possessed a compassionate heart that longed to make a difference in the lives of others. Inspired by the teachings of Jesus, Lily yearned to follow in his humble footsteps and serve those in need, just as he had done.

One day, Lily heard about a local soup kitchen that provided meals for the homeless and hungry in her community. Filled with excitement and determination, she eagerly volunteered her time and energy to the cause. With her parents' support, Lily embarked on a journey of humility and servanthood.

Upon entering the soup kitchen, Lily was greeted with bustling activity. The aroma of warm soup and freshly baked bread filled the air, embracing her with a sense of purpose. She donned an apron and joined the dedicated team of volunteers, ready to offer assistance wherever needed.

Lily soon discovered that her role extended beyond serving food. She listened attentively to the stories and struggles of the individuals who entered the soup kitchen, offering a kind word and a listening ear. Her genuine care and compassion touched hearts and sparked hope in the lives of those she encountered.

As days turned into weeks, Lily humbly recognized that her service went beyond mere tasks and responsibilities. She realized the profound impact of small acts of kindness—washing dishes with gratitude, offering a warm smile, and treating each person with dignity and respect.

One cold winter evening, the soup kitchen faced an unexpectedly high turnout. The staff and volunteers worked tirelessly, but they struggled to keep up with the demand. Lily, fueled by her determination to make a difference, stepped forward with a humble heart.

In the spirit of Jesus' example, Lily initiated a prayer circle, inviting everyone to gather and seek divine guidance. With bowed heads and open hearts, they sought strength and direction. In the midst of their prayers, an overwhelming sense of peace and calm filled the room.

Suddenly, a local bakery owner arrived with an abundance of freshly baked muffins and pastries. Their prayers had been answered. The volunteers stood in awe, witnessing the power of God's providence and the impact of their united hearts.

Inspired by this miraculous gesture, Lily and the other volunteers persisted in their service with even greater dedication. The soup kitchen became a place of not only physical nourishment but spiritual nourishment too—a haven where individuals felt seen, loved, and valued as they were.

In time, Lily's humble servant's heart became a guiding light for others. Her friends and family noticed the transformative impact her volunteer work had on her life. Inspired by her example, they joined her in serving the community, expanding the ripple of love and humility that began with one young girl's compassionate heart.

Years later, the soup kitchen flourished, not just as a place of nourishment, but as a center of hope and transformation. The spirit of humble service embodied by Lily and her fellow volunteers continued to touch lives, echoing the very essence of Jesus' teachings.

And so, the story of Lily, the humble servant, serves as a timeless reminder of the power of humility and selfless service. It teaches us that by mirroring Jesus' example, we can make a substantial impact in the lives of others, fostering a more compassionate and loving world.

The Compassionate Doctor

In a bustling city filled with busy streets and towering buildings, a child named Ethan had a dream that transcended the ordinary. He wished to become a doctor—a compassionate healer who could touch lives and bring comfort to those in need. Inspired by God's love and kindness, Ethan embarked on a journey to fulfill his calling.

From a young age, Ethan immersed himself in books about medicine and healing. He listened attentively as his parents shared stories of the selfless doctors they had encountered and the impact they had made. Their words ignited a fire within him—an unyielding determination to make a difference in the lives of others.

As Ethan grew older, he dedicated his time to studying hard, seeking guidance from experienced doctors, and learning the fundamental principles of medicine. His passion was fueled by a deep faith in God, knowing that his desire to heal others was an extension of God's love manifested through his own hands.

Ethan's dreams took shape when he was accepted into medical school. With joy and gratitude, he embraced the years of rigorous training ahead. Ethan learned not only the technical skills required to practice medicine but also the importance of empathy and compassion—pillars upon which true healing is built.

Upon graduating, Dr. Ethan Thompson began his medical career at a local hospital. Armed with knowledge, skills, and an unwavering faith, he embarked on a path paved with countless opportunities to touch lives and bring healing.

Every day, Dr. Ethan treated his patients not only with medical expertise but also with genuine care and love. He listened intently to their stories, offering a shoulder to lean on and a comforting presence. Driven by his deep-rooted faith, he shared with them the hope and strength that were borne out of his relationship with God.

Dr. Ethan's genuine compassion and healing touch soon became well-known throughout the community. Families sought him out from far and wide, confident in his ability to provide expert medical care intertwined with love and understanding.

Yet, Dr. Ethan's impact extended beyond the walls of the hospital. He engaged in medical missions, traveling to remote villages where access to healthcare was limited. With a team of like-minded professionals, he offered medical services to those desperately in need. His selfless acts of service and genuine care mirrored God's love for all His children.

Years passed, and Dr. Ethan's legacy lived on through the countless lives he had touched. His compassionate approach to medicine inspired younger generations to pursue healthcare with a God-centered mindset. The ripple effect of his actions expanded, touching the lives of patients, fellow doctors, and even those in entirely different professions.

As Dr. Ethan reflected on his journey, he marveled at the way God had worked through him. His dream of becoming a doctor had transformed into a passionate ministry—a calling to bring healing not just to physical bodies but also to hearts and spirits.

And so, the story of Dr. Ethan Thompson, the compassionate doctor, reminds us that the pursuit of medicine is more than a profession—it is an opportunity to demonstrate God's love, kindness, and healing touch. It encourages us to approach our vocations with love and compassion, knowing that even the simplest act of care can make a profound impact and illuminate the presence of God's unending love in our world.

The Wise Giver

In a small village nestled amidst rolling hills, there lived a curious and compassionate young boy named Noah. Although his family had modest means, Noah possessed a heart overflowing with generosity. He was captivated by the idea of bringing joy to others through the act of giving.

One summer evening, as Noah walked through the village square, he stumbled upon a gathering led by an elderly man known as Mr. Tobias. Mr. Tobias was sharing tales of his travels and the wisdom he had gained. Moved by his words, Noah approached him, eager to learn more about the art of giving.

With a twinkle in his eyes, Mr. Tobias sensed Noah's genuine desire to make a difference. He shared with Noah the principle of cheerful generosity—the idea that giving sacrificially brings immense joy, and that true abundance resides in sharing rather than accumulating.

Intrigued, Noah decided to embark on a journey of his own—a mission to discover the joy of giving and experience the principle of cheerful generosity firsthand. He started small by sharing his toys with neighborhood children, witnessing their smiles and laughter. The sense of fulfillment Noah experienced was indescribable.

As Noah progressed on his journey, he discovered that cheerful generosity meant giving not only material possessions but also time, attention, and acts of kindness. He volunteered at the local animal shelter, caring for abandoned pets, and offered a helping hand to elderly neighbors in need.

One fateful day, Noah learned of a family in the village that had fallen on hard times. Their home had been destroyed by a devastating storm, leaving them with no roof over their heads. Noah felt a deep sense of empathy and knew he had the opportunity to make a significant impact.

Determined to help, Noah gathered resources, mobilized the community, and led the efforts to rebuild the family's home. Through the collaboration and support of his neighbors, the family received a new home that surpassed their wildest dreams.

The joy and sense of fulfillment Noah experienced upon seeing the gratitude and happiness in the family's eyes were immeasurable. Through his sacrificial giving, he had discovered the true meaning of abundance—a wealth found in the act of sharing and making a difference in the lives of others.

News of Noah's acts of cheerful generosity spread throughout the village, inspiring others to adopt the same mindset. The village transformed into a community marked by compassion, selflessness, and an enduring spirit of giving.

Years passed, and Noah's legacy lived on. The village continued to thrive in the spirit of cheerful generosity, embracing the principle that true abundance can be found in sharing one's blessings. Noah's journey had touched countless lives, igniting a ripple effect of kindness and compassion that extended far beyond the village and into neighboring communities.

And so, the story of Noah, the wise giver, reminds us that true abundance is not measured by the amount of possessions we gather, but by the impact we make in the lives of others through cheerful generosity. Through his selfless acts, Noah had embraced the joy of giving sacrificially and discovered the true wealth that comes from sharing with those in need.

The Patient Farmer

In a picturesque countryside blessed with fertile soil and gentle sunlight, there lived a young farmer named Ava. With a heart full of dreams and a love for the land, Ava toiled diligently, tending to her crops with tender care.

As each season unfolded, Ava planted her seeds with hope and excitement. She eagerly awaited the sight of tender sprouts emerging from the earth, dreaming of the bountiful harvest that lay ahead. But often, the harvest did not come as quickly as she had anticipated.

Year after year, Ava faced the challenges that beset every farmer. Pests invaded her fields, storms threatened to destroy her hard work, and the changing weather patterns presented unexpected obstacles. Yet, through it all, Ava remained steadfast and patient, knowing that growth required time, perseverance, and faith.

On her quiet mornings in the field, Ava observed the delicate balance of nature, the symphony of life unfolding around her. She marveled at the intricate process of growth—the seeds transforming into mighty plants, the blossoms yielding fruits. The experience taught her a valuable lesson about God's timing, reminding her of the beauty that unfolds when things happen in their own natural rhythm.

Ava also found solace in the teachings of her community's faith. She realized that, just as her crops needed time to grow and mature, there were moments in her own life where patience and trust in God's timing were essential. She found peace in surrendering her worries and anxieties, understanding that everything had its purpose and would come to fruition in due time.

One particularly challenging season, Ava faced a drought that threatened her entire harvest. She watched as the soil cracked and the plants withered, her heart heavy with concern. But even in the face of adversity, Ava's faith remained unshaken. She offered prayers of gratitude for the lessons she had learned and sought guidance in her time of need.

Then, just when she thought all hope was lost, dark clouds gathered overhead, and droplets of rain began to fall. The gentle rain rejuvenated the parched earth, quenching the thirst of Ava's crops. The skies that had been barren for so long now poured forth life-giving water. In that moment, Ava knew the importance of faith and perseverance.

The following season, Ava witnessed an abundant harvest—a testament to God's faithfulness and the rewards of patience and trust. The fields teemed with fruits and vegetables, each one a testament to her diligent care and unwavering faith.

As word of Ava's bountiful harvest spread, neighboring farmers sought her advice and marveled at her perseverance. Ava humbly shared her experiences, emphasizing the vital role of patience and a deep-rooted faith in God's plan.

Through her journey as a patient farmer, Ava realized that life, like the growth of crops, required patience, steadfastness, and trust in the timing of the Divine. She continued to tend to her fields with love and care, knowing that the lessons she had learned would serve her well in all aspects of life.

And so, the story of Ava, the patient farmer, reminds us of the importance of trusting God's timing and the rewards that come with perseverance and faith. Just as the seeds need time to grow and the plants require patience to bear fruit, so too do our dreams and aspirations in life. By nurturing a spirit of patience and trust, we can witness the beauty and abundance that unfold when we surrender to God's perfect plan.

The Lost Note

In a quiet, cozy town nestled among rolling hills, a young boy named Daniel had a deep love for music and a curious spirit. One summer day, while exploring his grandmother's attic, he stumbled upon an old, weathered hymn book. Its pages were yellowed with age, hinting at the stories they held within.

As Daniel gently opened the hymn book, a small note slipped out and fell onto the floor at his feet. Intrigued, he unfolded the crumpled paper, revealing a hidden message inked in faded letters: "Follow the notes, seek His promises, find the true treasure."

Heart pounding with excitement, Daniel read the words over and over, trying to decipher their meaning. He knew this was the beginning of an extraordinary adventure that lay before him.

With determination in his eyes, Daniel embarked on a treasure hunt, guided by the power of God's promises. His journey began at the old, rustic church where he found the hymn book. As he turned to the first hymn, he noticed that certain notes were highlighted—an E, a G, and a B-flat. They seemed to be a musical code leading him onward.

Daniel followed the notes, allowing their sweet melody to guide him through the town. Each destination unveiled a new promise, whispering of God's faithfulness and love. From the park filled with colorful flowers to the lake reflecting the radiant sunset, he uncovered treasures in the most unexpected places.

The last note in the hymn book led Daniel to a secluded garden behind the church, blanketed in a tranquil stillness. As he stood there, awestruck, he discovered a hidden compartment within a weathered tree stump. Inside, he found a small wooden box intricately carved with symbols of faith—a true treasure indeed.

With trembling hands, Daniel opened the box and gasped at what lay inside—a collection of handwritten notes, each one filled with powerful promises from God's Word. It was a treasure trove of comfort, guidance, and hope.

Overwhelmed with gratitude, Daniel realized that this adventure was not just about finding physical treasures. It was about discovering the immeasurable riches of God's promises and the unshakable joy that came from embracing them.

With a heart full of joy, Daniel returned to the church and shared his experience with the community. He encouraged others to seek the treasure of God's promises, reminding them of the power and comfort found within His Word.

From that day forward, the old hymn book became a cherished possession, passed down through generations as a reminder of God's faithfulness. Each note Daniel had discovered served as a testament to the eternal promises that guided their lives.

And so, the story of Daniel's treasure hunt lived on, reminding people to seek God's promises in every season of life. It taught them that the true treasure is not found in material possessions, but in the promises of love, grace, and eternal life that God lavishes upon His children.

The Mysterious Painting

In a charming village adorned with cobblestone streets and colorful houses, a child named Emily loved to explore the world through her vivid imagination. One day, while wandering through the local park, she noticed an elderly artist, Mr. Jacob, sitting on a bench with a captivating painting by his side - one that seemed to emit an inexplicable aura.

Intrigued by the masterpiece, Emily approached Mr. Jacob and struck up a conversation. Little did she know that this chance encounter would lead her on a wondrous journey of faith and learning. Mr. Jacob, with a twinkle in his eyes, whispered that this painting had a mysterious secret. It had the power to bring biblical stories to life.

In awe and anticipation, Emily watched as Mr. Jacob gently touched the surface of the painting. Suddenly, the canvas shimmered, and Emily found herself standing within the vibrant world of the Bible—a realm where miracles and parables unfolded before her eyes.

She witnessed Moses parting the Red Sea, felt the strength of David as he faced Goliath, and heard Jesus speaking in the Sermon on the Mount. Each time, she marveled at the mystical power of the painting, absorbing the valuable lessons and deepening her faith.

As Emily continued her encounters with the miraculous painting, she learned about the significance of God's promises and the importance of trust and obedience. The stories came alive before her, leaving an indelible imprint on her young heart.

Eager to share her newfound knowledge, Emily gathered her friends and family. They joined her in front of the magical painting, experiencing its transformative power together. Through each story, they learned valuable lessons of compassion, forgiveness, and the boundless love of God.

Word of the painting's mystical nature and the lessons it imparted spread through the village. Families far and wide came to witness the enchantment, drawing people together in unity and faith. It formed a bond, transcending age, background, and generations.

But one day, as Emily visited the park, she found Mr. Jacob's bench empty. A note attached to the easel revealed that Mr. Jacob had passed into eternity, leaving behind a legacy of art and faith. However, his final wish had been fulfilled—a wish for the painting to continue bringing biblical stories to life.

With a mix of sorrow and gratitude, Emily stepped forward, deeply understanding the responsibility resting upon her young shoulders. With each touch of the painting, she carried on Mr. Jacob's legacy, sharing the vibrant stories, and nurturing the faith of those who witnessed their miraculous reenactments.

And so, Emily dedicated herself to keeping the painting alive, allowing its supernatural power to teach, inspire, and transform hearts. The mysterious painting became a beacon of faith, forever reminding the village—and all who encountered it—of the deep message and eternal truths found within God's Word.

As the years passed and generations changed, Emily continued to protect and preserve the magical painting. Its lessons of faith and trust persevered, bringing light and illumination to all who embraced its enchantment. And so, the story of the mysterious painting lives on, immersing people in the wonders of biblical narratives, nurturing their faith, and reminding them of the boundless power of God's word.

The Bold Truth

In a bustling city filled with diverse cultures and ideologies, two inseparable friends named Sara and James faced a challenge that tested their resolve. As devoted followers of Jesus, they openly expressed their faith in their daily lives. Their genuine care and love for others radiated from their hearts, drawing people towards them.

However, as time passed, they encountered opposition from a few who disagreed with their beliefs. Some mocked their faith, while others questioned its relevance in the modern world. Sara and James felt disheartened, but instead of retreating, they decided to stand boldly for the truth.

With unwavering faith, they sought guidance from God's Word, finding comfort and strength within its pages. They discovered stories of other believers who had faced similar challenges and remained steadfast in their commitment to God.

Armed with this newfound courage, Sara and James resolved to share God's love and truth with even greater fervor. They engaged in respectful conversations, sharing personal anecdotes and biblical wisdom. Their intention was not to argue or impose, but to open hearts to the transformative power of God's love.

As they persevered, they found that their boldness in sharing the truth began to soften hearts, prompting sincere questions and deep conversations. Many individuals, captivated by the authenticity of Sara and James, embraced God's love and experienced a profound transformation within.

However, despite their efforts, opposition continued to persist. Sara and James faced ridicule and sometimes felt isolated in their faith. In these moments, they reminded themselves of God's promise: "Blessed are those who are persecuted for righteousness' sake, for theirs is the kingdom of heaven."

Encouraged by this truth, Sara and James sought solace in their friendship and in the company of like-minded believers. They organized small gatherings where they could support one another, uplift each other in prayer, and share testimonies of God's faithfulness.

Over time, word of their unwavering faith spread throughout the city, touching the hearts of many. In the face of adversity, Sara and James modeled Christ's love and compassion, challenging common misconceptions and igniting a spark of curiosity in those who had once questioned their faith.

The impact of their bold truth extended far beyond their imagination. Families reconciled, forgiveness was offered, and communities experienced the transformative power of God's love. Through their dedication to remaining true to God's Word, Sara and James witnessed miracles of healing and restoration in the lives of those they encountered.

As the years rolled by, Sara and James' faith became a beacon of light in the city. Their love for God and their love for others continued to guide their actions and inspire others to pursue truth with boldness.

Their story became a reminder for all believers—that even in the face of opposition, remaining true to God's Word and sharing His love with others can create a powerful ripple effect, transforming lives and communities.

And so, the story of Sara and James stands as a testament to the importance of standing up for one's faith, no matter the challenges that arise. Their brave act of sharing God's love and truth in the face of opposition inspires generations to follow their example, knowing that when truth is coupled with genuine love, lives can be forever changed and the world can be touched by God's redeeming grace.

The Silenced Songbird

In a quaint village nestled amidst rolling hills and blossoming meadows, a young girl named Lily delighted in the enchantment of nature. Her heart overflowed with love and compassion for the creatures that filled the air with their melodic tunes. But one day, as she ventured into the nearby forest, she encountered a scene that filled her with sadness—a wounded songbird lay helpless, its once vibrant feathers now dull and lifeless.

Rushing to the bird's side, Lily gently cupped it in her hands, her heart aching with empathy. She knew she had to help this fragile creature. With tenderness and care, she carried the bird home, dedicating herself to its healing and restoration.

Lily transformed a corner of her room into a sanctuary, filling it with fresh branches, soft moss, and a cozy nest for the injured bird. She bathed the bird's wounds with warm water and nourished it with seeds and berries. Every day, Lily whispered words of comfort and encouragement, sharing her love and compassion as she nursed the fragile creature back to health.

As the days turned into weeks, the bird's feathers regained their luster, and its once feeble chirps echoed with newfound strength. Lily marveled at the transformation—a testament to the amazing power of healing and restoration.

But there was something more profound that Lily discovered through this experience. As she nurtured the injured bird, she sensed a divine presence—the gentle touch of God's love. She learned that just as she had cared for the wounded bird, God's love brings comfort and restoration to all who are hurting.

In moments of doubt and uncertainty, Lily turned to prayer and sought solace in the beauty of nature, finding reassurance in God's faithfulness. She realized that God's love knows no bounds, reaching even the smallest creatures of the Earth. The bird became a symbol of God's tender care and a reminder of His presence in her life.

When the time came for the bird's release, Lily could hardly contain her joy. With tears of gratitude streaming down her face, she opened the door of the sanctuary and watched as the once wounded bird spread its wings, soaring into the sky with newfound strength.

From that day forward, Lily carried the lessons of healing and restoration in her heart. She became a beacon of compassion, extending God's love to all those who needed healing—both physical and emotional. In the most unexpected ways, she brought comfort and restoration to those around her, just as she had witnessed with the silencing of the wounded songbird.

And so, the story of the silenced songbird continued to resonate throughout the village and beyond, a gentle reminder of the profound healing and restoration that can come from God's love. Through Lily's acts of compassion, the wounded found comfort, the broken found restoration, and the world was touched by the miraculous power of God's abiding love.

The Grateful Journey

In a quaint town nestled amidst picturesque landscapes, the Anderson family, consisting of Mr. and Mrs. Anderson and their two children, Sarah and Ethan, embarked on a remarkable road trip—a journey filled with gratitude, appreciation, and a deepening connection with God.

As they set off in their trusty family car, their hearts were filled with anticipation. The radio played uplifting songs that filled the vehicle with joyful melodies, setting the tone for their adventure. Mr. Anderson drove, while Mrs. Anderson navigated the winding roads with a sense of wonder.

Their chosen route meandered through breathtaking scenery—majestic mountains, serene lakes, and vibrant fields. The family made frequent stops, taking the time to soak in the beauty of God's creation and express gratitude for the blessings they had been bestowed.

During their first stop at a shimmering lake, Sarah and Ethan delighted in skipping stones across the water, the ripples reflecting their joy and gratitude. They counted their blessings, mentioning things they were grateful for—a loving family, the warmth of the sun, and the opportunity to embark on this journey together.

As the road trip progressed, the family found new and awe-inspiring sights around every corner. They marveled at cascading waterfalls, fragrant meadows, and the awe-inspiring grandeur of ancient forests. Each stop served as a reminder of the vastness and diversity of God's creation, evoking a deep sense of gratitude within their hearts.

At each destination, the family paused to offer prayers of thanksgiving. They recognized God's presence in the smallest details—the intricate design of a flower petal, the melody of birdsong, and the gentle caress of a passing breeze. Their journey became a gratitude-filled pilgrimage, a testament to the power of recognizing and appreciating God's blessings.

As the final days of their road trip approached, the Anderson family reflected upon their experiences. Sarah and Ethan shared how the journey had deepened their faith, broadened their perspectives, and cultivated a sense of appreciation for the wonders of God's creation. They realized that gratitude was not simply about giving thanks, but a way to honor and connect with God on a personal level.

Upon returning home, the Anderson family carried the spirit of the grateful journey with them. They embraced the practice of expressing gratitude daily, cherishing each sunrise, sunset, and moment shared as a family. Their road trip had not only created lasting memories but instilled in them an enduring gratitude that would continue to shape their lives.

And so, the story of the grateful journey lived on—a testament to the transformative power of expressing gratitude and appreciating God's beautiful creation. It serves as a gentle reminder to perceive each day as an opportunity for thanksgiving and recognition of His blessings, fostering a lifelong journey grounded in deep gratitude and love.

The Rescued Pup

In a quiet neighborhood nestled amidst rolling hills, a lonely dog named Buddy roamed the streets, searching for a place to call home. With each passing day, his spirits diminished, and his heart grew heavy. Buddy longed for love, warmth, and the comfort of a loving family.

One fateful afternoon, as Buddy wandered near a bustling park, he caught the attention of a kind-hearted family—the Martins. Mrs. Martin, with her gentle eyes filled with compassion, immediately recognized Buddy's longing for connection. She beckoned the family to pause, urging them to approach the weary dog with care.

As they approached, Buddy's tail wagged tentatively, unsure of what kindness lay before him. But the Martins showered him with gentle words and patience, gradually earning his trust. They extended their hands, offering love and warmth that Buddy had longed for.

Moved by Buddy's plight and captivated by his gentle nature, the Martins decided to bring him into their loving home. They nurtured him back to health, providing him with a soft bed, nourishing food, and an abundance of affection. Buddy blossomed under their care, his once sad eyes now filled with an unmistakable sparkle of gratitude.

In turn, Buddy became a profound teacher for the Martins. With his unwavering loyalty and the unconditional love he showered upon them, the family learned the value of compassion, empathy, and care for all of God's creations. They realized that extending love and kindness to animals was a reflection of the love poured out by their Creator.

The Martins' gratitude for Buddy's presence grew each day, their hearts overwhelmed by the joy and warmth he brought into their lives. They now understood that kindness was not limited to human connections but encompassed every living being. They became ardent advocates for animal rescue causes, spreading awareness about the importance of providing love and care to abandoned pets.

As news of Buddy's incredible transformation and the compassionate hearts of the Martins spread throughout the community, others were inspired to follow suit. The community rallied together, organizing adoption drives, supporting local shelters, and advocating for the welfare of animals.

Buddy's presence in the Martins' home served as a reminder to the family and the community that showing compassion and care to all creatures was a testament to the goodness of God's creation. Buddy's journey from abandonment to a life filled with love and purpose became a symbol of second chances, redemption, and the power of compassion.

And so, the story of Buddy, The Rescued Pup, lived on—a testament to the transformative power of love, compassion, and empathy. It taught the Martins and the community that, in showing kindness to all creatures, they were not only fulfilling their responsibility as caretakers but also embodying the love that God pours out upon all living beings.

The Caring Cupcake Stand

Once upon a time in a small, bustling town named Sweetville, there were two best friends named Lily and Emma. They were kind-hearted and always looked for ways to help others. One day, while walking through the town square, they noticed a notice pinned to a bulletin board that grabbed their attention. It said, "Help those in need - Start a cupcake stand!"

Lily and Emma lit up with excitement. They both loved baking and realized this could be an incredible opportunity to bring joy to others while raising money for a good cause. They quickly made their way to Grandma Daisy's kitchen to seek her advice and learn her delicious cupcake recipes.

With Grandma Daisy's recipes in their hands, the girls were ready to embark on their sweet journey. They pooled their savings to buy the necessary ingredients and baking supplies. They set up their cupcake stand in the heart of Sweetville, next to the town square, on a sunny Saturday morning.

Their stand, appropriately named "The Caring Cupcake Stand," was adorned with colorful banners and signs that read, "Cupcakes for a Cause." Their goal was to raise money to support a local charity that helped families in need. With their aprons on and smiles on their faces, Lily and Emma eagerly awaited their first customers.

Word spread quickly throughout Sweetville about the Caring Cupcake Stand. People were drawn not only to the delicious cupcakes but also to the girls' enthusiasm and their mission to make a difference. The town's residents flocked to the stand, eager to support Lily and Emma's cause.

As one customer after another visited the cupcake stand, Lily and Emma were touched by the stories they shared. They met families who were struggling to put food on their tables, single parents working multiple jobs to make ends meet, and children in need of warm clothes and school supplies. These encounters made the girls even more committed to their cause.

Seeing the impact they could make, Lily and Emma worked tirelessly day after day, mixing batter, frosting cupcakes, and serving customers with kindness and compassion. Their cupcake stand became a symbol of hope and generosity in Sweetville.

News of their good deeds spread beyond Sweetville. Local news outlets highlighted Lily and Emma's selfless act, inspiring people from neighboring towns and cities to support the Caring Cupcake Stand. Cupcake enthusiasts across the region paid visits and even ordered cupcakes to be delivered.

Soon enough, the cups of kindness overflowed. The Caring Cupcake Stand succeeded in raising an astonishing amount of money. Lily and Emma were thrilled, but they knew their journey did not end there. They gathered all the funds they had raised and organized a community event to present their donation to the local charity.

The day of the presentation arrived, and Lily and Emma, flanked by their families and friends, handed over a giant check with a smile. The local charity representatives couldn't believe their eyes. The girls' small act of generosity had snowballed into a significant amount that would make a real impact on the lives of those in need.

With gratitude in their hearts, Lily and Emma thanked everyone who had supported their cause. They learned that even the smallest acts of kindness could make a world of difference. The power of their cupcakes brought joy to others, and they were proud to have made a positive change in their community.

From that day forward, Lily and Emma continued their mission of spreading kindness and helping those in need. The Caring Cupcake Stand became a permanent fixture in Sweetville, serving not only delicious treats but also a reminder that everyone can make a difference, one cupcake at a time.

The Sparkling Stars

Once upon a time, in a small village nestled amongst rolling hills, there lived a young girl named Maya. Maya was a curious and thoughtful girl with gleaming, almond-shaped eyes that sparkled with wonder. She loved spending her evenings stargazing, finding solace and peace under the vast canopy of the night sky.

One evening, as Maya lay on the grass, her gaze fixed upon the twinkling stars, she couldn't help but wonder about the wonders of the world. Feeling a deep longing in her heart, she whispered, "What is the purpose of our existence? Is there something greater connecting us all?"

To her surprise, a gentle voice resonated in her mind, "Look closer, my dear child, and you shall see."

Intrigued by the mysterious voice, Maya ventured out every night, searching for answers while admiring the celestial beauty above. One night, while she lay beneath a particularly bright star, she fell into a deep slumber.

As her dreams unfolded, Maya found herself floating amidst a serene meadow. The grass swayed gently beneath her feet as a vibrant tapestry of flowers danced in the breeze. Curiously, she noticed a gathering of people from different backgrounds, each adorned with unique attire and speaking various languages. Yet, there was an energy that united them all.

"Welcome, Maya," a soft voice whispered. Startled, she looked around to see an old man with a kind face. "Fear not, my child. I am here to guide you."

He introduced himself as Elijah, a wise sage who had traveled the world in search of understanding. He explained that each person present represented the diverse threads that weave the fabric of humanity.

Maya's heart swelled with awe as Elijah shared stories of human compassion, resilience, and love. The people's tales fostered in her a deep appreciation for their differences, and she realized that the unity she sought had been present all along.

Elijah guided Maya to a hilltop where they could gaze upon the starlit sky. "What do you see?" he asked.

Maya stared intently, realizing that each star, though unique in size and brilliance, illuminated the dark expanse. Just as the stars formed constellations creating mesmerizing patterns, humans too had the power to create magical connections.

Elijah explained, "Just as stars shine from within, so too does each person carry a divine spark. When we embrace our differences and recognize the beauty in others, we witness God's love shining through."

This revelation filled Maya's heart with joy. Inspired by the unity and diversity she had experienced, she returned to her village, eager to share her newfound understanding.

Maya's village had always been harmonious, where people respected each other's beliefs and traditions. But now, her perspective had shifted, and she longed to deepen the connections between villagers even further.

With enthusiasm, Maya organized gatherings in the village square. People from various backgrounds shared their stories, songs, and dances. They celebrated their differences and discovered common threads that bound them together.

As Maya looked around, she saw the stars in each person's eyes, radiating with the same divine love she had witnessed in her dreams. Families who were once strangers became lifelong friends, and the village flourished, becoming a shining example of unity and acceptance.

Maya's love for stargazing remained, and she continued to share her insight with others. As she journeyed through life, she reminded everyone to look up, to see the heavens mirrored in their hearts, and to embrace the beautiful symphony of diversity and unity.

And so, the village of Maya became a beacon of love, where every person was cherished as a precious star in the infinite sky of humanity.

The Hidden Talents

O nce upon a time in the small town of Serendipity Springs, there was a classroom full of misfit classmates who often felt like they didn't quite fit in. They were each unique in their own ways, but their differences made it difficult for them to find their place among their peers. However, little did they know that their differences were not weaknesses, but hidden talents waiting to be discovered.

In this group, there was Oliver, a shy and introverted boy who loved to draw; Amelia, a free-spirited girl with an incredible knack for solving puzzles; Marcus, a smart and curious boy who could fix just about anything; and Sofia, a thoughtful and empathetic girl with a soothing voice that soothed even the most troubled hearts.

One sunny day, their class received a new teacher named Ms. Johnson. Ms. Johnson was unlike any teacher they had ever encountered. She recognized their talents and made it her mission to help them discover their hidden gifts. She believed that God had given each of them a purpose and a role to play in His plans.

Ms. Johnson introduced the class to various activities and challenges, encouraging them to think outside the box and embrace their individual strengths. They soon found joy and fulfillment in their newfound passions. Oliver's drawings came to life, capturing the essence of people's emotions and bringing them solace during difficult times. Amelia's puzzle-solving skills proved invaluable in finding innovative solutions to everyday problems. Marcus's ability to fix things extended beyond objects as he became a trusted helper, mending hearts with his wisdom and compassion. Sofia's soothing voice became an instrument of healing, bringing calmness and serenity to anyone who heard it.

As they continued their journey of self-discovery, the misfit classmates realized that their talents complemented each other perfectly. They became a close-knit group, supporting and encouraging one another as they faced the challenges they encountered.

One day, a local community center was facing a crisis. The center was a hub for people seeking refuge, support, and a sense of belonging. Its resources were dwindling, and it was on the verge of closing down. Upon hearing this, Oliver, Amelia, Marcus, and Sofia knew they had to put their talents to use and help save this vital place.

Together, they organized a fundraising event, showcasing their individual gifts. Oliver displayed his artwork, capturing the emotions and stories of the community members. Amelia created an elaborate puzzle solving competition, bringing people together to overcome challenges. Marcus fixed broken appliances and offered his guidance to whoever sought his help. Sofia's voice filled the hall, creating an atmosphere of peace and unity.

Their event was a grand success. The entire town came together, captivated by the talents of these misfit classmates. The funds poured in, renewing hope in the hearts of the community center's supporters. As a result, not only did they save the community center, but they also revived the spirits of the people it served.

Through their efforts, the misfit classmates finally understood the importance of their unique talents. They realized that God had given them these gifts not just for personal fulfillment but to make a difference in the lives of others. From that day forward, they dedicated themselves to using their talents to bring about positive change, knowing that no matter how different they were, they would always find strength and purpose in their united mission.

And so, the misfit classmates continued to inspire and uplift those around them, sharing their talents and spreading God's love throughout Serendipity Springs. They taught the town that everyone has hidden gifts waiting to be discovered and that in embracing those gifts, they would find their true purpose in God's great design.

The Compassionate Athlete

Once upon a time, in a small town nestled at the foot of a majestic mountain range, lived a young athlete named Alex. Alex was known for his incredible talent and unwavering determination. He had dreams of becoming the best athlete in his chosen field and making his town proud. He always strived to push his limits and inspire those around him.

One fateful day, just as Alex was on the cusp of realizing his dreams, tragedy struck. During a crucial competition, he suffered a severe injury, shattering not only his hopes but also his spirit. The doctors told him it would take months, maybe even years, to recover. The setback left him despondent and filled with self-doubt.

As days turned into weeks, Alex found himself consumed by anger and frustration. He withdrew from his friends, family, and the world of sports that he once loved. But little did he know that the compassion of others had not deserted him.

One afternoon, while sitting alone in his room, reflecting on his shattered dreams, there was a knock at the door. Nick, a fellow athlete and friend, stood before him with a somber expression. Nick had heard about Alex's injury and had come to offer his support.

He shared the story of a great athlete he had once admired, who had faced adversity but had emerged stronger. Nick encouraged Alex to draw strength from within, to use this setback as an opportunity for growth. Alex listened intently, and slowly his spirit began to reawaken.

With Nick's unwavering support behind him, Alex decided to channel his energy into helping others. He volunteered at the local community center, coaching young athletes and sharing his knowledge and passion for sports. Despite his own frustrations, Alex used his time to instill good sportsmanship values, forgiveness, and compassion in those he mentored.

Months passed, and as Alex immersed himself in helping others, he realized that the true essence of sportsmanship wasn't found solely in winning but in helping others reach their full potential. He became the embodiment of compassion, guiding his young students to cultivate a love for the sport and showing them how to overcome setbacks with resilience and a caring nature.

Word of Alex's newfound compassion and dedication spread throughout the town. People were inspired by his story and began to look up to him, not just for his athletic accomplishments but for the way he had transformed his own adversity into an avenue for generosity and kindness. Slowly but surely, the entire community rallied behind him, supporting him in his recovery and cheering him on as he prepared to make his comeback.

Months turned into years, and Alex defied all expectations. With the help of his friends, family, and the newfound compassion he had embraced, he made a remarkable recovery. His love for the sport had only grown stronger, and this time, he approached it with a newfound humility and strength of character.

Finally, the day of his comeback competition arrived. As he stepped onto the field, he looked around at the familiar faces that had supported him through his darkest hours. They held signs that read, "Compassion is the true path to victory" and "You inspire us, Alex!"

With every stride, Alex showcased not only his skill but also his indomitable spirit and compassionate heart. Even though he didn't place first, the audience erupted in a thunderous applause that echoed throughout the stadium. The real victory had been achieved – the victory of triumphing over personal setbacks, of demonstrating the importance of sportsmanship, forgiveness, and caring for others.

From that day forward, Alex was known as "The Compassionate Athlete," a beacon of inspiration for all young athletes who faced adversity. He continued to teach the values of compassion and sportsmanship, and his story lived on as a reminder that true victory is not merely defined by trophies but by the positive impact we have on others.

The Guardian Angel

Once upon a time in a quiet town lived a boy named Ethan. Ethan was a shy and timid boy, often feeling overwhelmed in social situations and constantly plagued by fears. He never quite found the courage to face his fears head-on, which made even the simplest tasks seem insurmountable for him.

One fateful evening, as Ethan lay in bed pondering his fears, a gentle light filled his room. Startled, he sat up and saw a figure standing before him. The figure had a calming presence and a warm smile that immediately put Ethan at ease.

"I am your Guardian Angel," the figure said softly. "I have been sent to help you overcome your fears and navigate difficult situations."

Ethan couldn't believe his luck. He had heard stories about angels but had never thought he would have his very own guardian. From that moment on, Ethan and his angel, whom he named Gabriel, became the best of friends.

Gabriel knew that for Ethan to grow and become confident, he needed to face his fears one by one. They began their journey by tackling Ethan's fear of speaking in class. Each day, Gabriel would whisper words of encouragement and wisdom into Ethan's ear just before he stood up to speak. With Gabriel's support, Ethan's voice grew stronger and his confidence began to soar.

Next, Gabriel helped Ethan face his fear of heights. They climbed to the top of the tallest tree in the neighborhood, with Gabriel reminding Ethan to trust in God's protection. As Ethan perched on the highest branch, he slowly overcame his fear, realizing that he was not alone, but surrounded by the love and guidance of his Guardian Angel.

As their bond deepened, Gabriel shared stories of other people who overcame their fears through faith. He reminded Ethan that courage was not the absence of fear, but rather the ability to push through despite it. Ethan learned that relying on God's protection and guidance was a source of strength and comfort in even the most difficult situations.

Together, Ethan and Gabriel faced many trials. Whether it was standing up to bullies, giving presentations, or trying out for the school play, Gabriel was always by Ethan's side, reminding him to trust in God's plan and to face his fears head-on. And each time, Ethan became a little braver, a little stronger.

As the years passed, Ethan grew into a confident and compassionate young man. His once timid nature had transformed into resilience and fearlessness. He became the voice for the voiceless, standing up for justice and helping those in need. His unwavering faith in God's protection and guidance became a beacon of light for others.

With Gabriel by his side, Ethan realized that he was never alone in his struggles. God had sent a guardian angel to help him navigate life's challenges and fears. And for that, he was forever grateful.

And so, the story of Ethan, the once shy boy who befriended a guardian angel, became an inspiration to all who heard it. It reminded them to have faith, to rely on God's protection and guidance, and to face their fears head-on with courage.

The Generosity Tree

Once upon a time in the heart of a small village, there stood a majestic and ancient tree. The tree had withstood the test of time, its gnarled branches reaching high into the sky. But what made this tree truly remarkable was its magical power to bloom with opportunities for children to give to others.

The news of this enchanted tree spread far and wide, reaching the ears of children from neighboring villages. Excitement twinkled in their eyes as they gathered around the tree, eager to witness its extraordinary magic. They marveled at the vibrant colors of its leaves and the scent of wonder that surrounded it.

Underneath the tree's sturdy trunk, a sign was placed which read, "The Joy of Generosity and Shared Blessings." The tree seemed to understand the language of the children's hearts. It would bless them with opportunities, and in return, it hoped to teach them the joy of giving to others.

One sunny morning, a young girl named Lily visited the tree with uncertainty gleaming in her eyes. She had never experienced the true meaning of generosity before. As if sensing her apprehension, the tree burst into a dazzling display of shimmering leaves and colorful blossoms.

Lily gasped and watched in awe as a small wooden box appeared in front of her. Curiosity brimming within her, she opened the box to find a handful of sparkling seeds. The tree whispered in her ear, "Plant these seeds wherever you see someone in need."

With newfound determination, Lily embarked on a heartfelt journey. She scattered seeds in forgotten gardens, where flowers bloomed and brought smiles to the faces of elderly inhabitants. She planted seeds near schools, where they grew into bountiful fruit trees for children to enjoy. In every act of generosity, Lily witnessed the joy it brought to others and felt her own heart swell with happiness.

Word of Lily's selfless acts spread throughout the village, inspiring other children to visit the magical tree. Among them was a boy named Oliver. Impressed by Lily's generosity, Oliver yearned to experience the joy of giving as well. As he approached the tree, it erupted into a symphony of leaves and petals showering the ground.

Oliver discovered a set of paintbrushes nestled within the fallen petals. The tree's voice whispered in his ear, "Bring color and happiness to the grayest corners of our world."

With the paintbrushes in his hands and a newfound purpose in his heart, Oliver set out to transform the village. He painted murals on aging walls, turning dull streets into vibrant galleries for all to enjoy. He filled abandoned spaces with colors and brought laughter to the faces of those who had long forgotten how to smile.

The magical tree continued to bloom with different opportunities for each child who came seeking its wisdom. The children learned valuable lessons about compassion, gratitude, and empathy. They discovered that the true magic of the tree lay not only in its ability to grant wishes but in the joy it brought to their own lives as they gave to others.

As time passed, the village, thanks to the children's efforts, became a community where generosity flourished. People would gather under the magical tree, sharing stories of their acts of kindness, and basking in the warmth of its ever-blooming branches.

And so, the magical tree stood tall, adorned with the laughter, love, and gratitude of the children and villagers alike. It became a beacon of hope, teaching generations that the biggest blessings are not in what we receive, but in what we give to others.

The Trusty Lighthouse

In a quaint coastal town, nestled between rugged cliffs and the vast expanse of the sea, stood an old and abandoned lighthouse. It was called "The Trusty Lighthouse," named after its days of glory when it faithfully guided sailors to safety. But now, its once radiant glow had dimmed, and its purpose forgotten.

One stormy night, a young sailor named Jack found himself in the midst of a tempestuous sea. Buffeted by raging winds and towering waves, he saw no light to lead him home. Fear gnawed at his heart as he desperately sought refuge from the merciless storm. Just when all hope seemed lost, he caught a glimpse of a faint beam shining from a distance.

Summoning every ounce of strength, Jack navigated his ship towards the ethereal light. With each passing moment, the light grew stronger, its radiance piercing through the gloom, and Jack's spirit lifted. Eventually, he found himself face-to-face with the once-forgotten Trusty Lighthouse.

As he stepped ashore, drenched and weary, Jack couldn't help but feel an inexplicable sense of awe. The lighthouse, though abandoned, emanated an air of tranquility and grace. He climbed the spiraling staircase, each step accompanied by a creaking sound echoing the stories of countless journeys it had witnessed. Reaching the top, Jack discovered a dusty room, filled with old books and a tattered Bible.

Curiosity sparked within him as he picked up the Bible, its pages worn and well-thumbed. Jack found solace in its words, finding comfort and timeless wisdom that seemed tailor-made for his weary soul. With each reading, he discovered that God's Word acted as a guiding light, illuminating his path amidst life's trials and tribulations.

Days turned into weeks, and weeks turned into months. Jack regularly visited the Trusty Lighthouse, seeking refuge from the storms that raged both outside and within. With each visit, he found the courage to confront his fears, the strength to persevere, and the wisdom to navigate life's tumultuous seas.

News of Jack's transformation traveled throughout the town, inviting others to come to witness the extraordinary power of the Trusty Lighthouse. The old lighthouse, filled with hope and purpose once more, welcomed seekers of solace and wayward souls like an enduring beacon of light.

People from all walks of life sought refuge within the lighthouse's walls. They discovered that within the pages of the Bible lay strength and healing, forgiveness and redemption. The Trusty Lighthouse became a sanctuary, where lost souls found guidance, hearts found peace, and spirits found renewal.

Years passed, and as time weathered the town and its inhabitants, the Trusty Lighthouse remained a symbol of unwavering faith. Though the storms of life came and went, the light within the lighthouse never waned. Its glow continued to guide those who sought direction, reminding them that even when surrounded by darkness, the light of God's Word would always guide them home.

And so, the Trusty Lighthouse became not just a physical structure but a testament to the enduring power of faith. It stood tall, illuminating the path for generations to come, reminding them that within the pages of God's Word lie the answers and guidance they seek.

The Miraculous Matchmaker

In a quiet little town, nestled amidst rolling hills and painted with a hue of nostalgia, lived a girl named Emily. Emily's grandmother, Elizabeth, was a kind-hearted woman who had spent many years feeling lonely after the passing of her beloved husband. Emily could see the longing in her grandmother's eyes for companionship, and she made it her mission to bring joy back into her life.

Emily believed in the wonder of miracles, and she would often find herself exploring the woods near their home, seeking solace and guidance. It was on one of those adventurous walks that Emily stumbled upon an old and weathered book. As she opened its pages, delicate script revealed a hint of magic within its words—a guide on how to unite lonely hearts.

With excitement pulsing through her veins, Emily realized that this book held the key to helping her grandmother find a companion. Eagerly flipping through its pages, she discovered that it emphasized the importance of patience, trust, and the perfect timing of God's provision for relationships.

Armed with newfound knowledge and determination, Emily set out on a mission. She spent hours listening to her grandmother's cherished stories of love, laughter, and lost years. Through their heartfelt conversations, Emily gained a deep understanding of the qualities her grandmother desired in a companion.

Emily began her search by introducing her grandmother to various community gatherings and social events. Elizabeth reluctantly agreed, embracing Emily's optimism. But despite their efforts, true connection eluded them.

Days turned into weeks, and still, there was no sign of the companion Elizabeth longed for. Disheartened, Emily turned to the magical book once again. Its pages whispered a reminder that true love and companionship are often discovered when least expected, in the most unlikely of places.

Inspired by this insight, Emily invited her grandmother on a spontaneous trip to the local park one sunny afternoon. Amidst the hustle and bustle of children playing and birds singing, Emily noticed an elderly man named George, sitting alone on a bench, his eyes filled with longing.

Emily mustered up her courage and walked over to George, engaging him in a warm conversation. She discovered that George had lost his wife many years ago and had been battling loneliness ever since. A spark of hope ignited within Emily's heart. Could it be that George was the companion her grandmother had been searching for?

With Elizabeth by her side, Emily introduced George to her grandmother. Their eyes met, and a sense of familiarity washed over them. As they exchanged stories and shared laughter, Emily knew that something special was happening—a connection that only God's hand could orchestrate.

Days turned into months, and a beautiful friendship blossomed between Elizabeth and George. They discovered shared interests, brought out the best in one another, and filled each other's lives with joy and companionship.

Emily and her grandmother marveled at the perfect timing and provision of God's grace. They learned that love sometimes arrives when we least expect it, but when we are open to His guidance, He brings individuals into our lives who are meant to journey alongside us.

As time passed, Emily witnessed the transformation in her grandmother's spirit. Elizabeth radiated a renewed sense of purpose and fulfillment, her heart brimming with gratitude for the miraculous matchmaker that Emily had become. Emily cherished the knowledge that, in her small act of kindness, she had helped two souls find solace and happiness.

The tale of Emily, Elizabeth, and George soon spread throughout the town, inspiring others to trust in God's perfect timing for their own relationships. The love that blossomed between Elizabeth and George became a steadfast reminder that sometimes, it is during our most patient and trusting moments that God's most extraordinary provisions are made known.

And so, the town marveled at the power of love, guided by the hands of a young girl who believed in miracles. Emily's lesson resonated within their hearts, reminding them to trust in God's timing and provision, knowing that love has a way of finding us when we least expect it.

The Reunited Friends

In a bustling city filled with noise and hurried hearts, two childhood friends named Sarah and Hannah lived separate lives, each carrying the weight of their own burdens. They had once been inseparable, sharing laughter and dreams, but as life's paths diverged, their friendship withered away like a forgotten flower. Years passed, and the distance between them grew wider, leaving behind memories bound by the echoes of lost time.

One fateful day, as golden sunlight filtered through the bustling city streets, Sarah found herself lost in bittersweet nostalgia. The ache of longing in her heart led her down a familiar road, bringing her to the park where she and Hannah used to spend endless afternoons. Standing beneath the towering oak tree they used to claim as their secret fortress, Sarah closed her eyes and whispered a prayer.

"Dear God, I miss my dear friend Hannah. If it be Your will, please reunite our hearts once more."

Unbeknownst to Sarah, Hannah had been carrying a similar longing in her own heart. The weight of regrets and lost years had taken their toll, leaving an empty void within her soul. In the solitude of her own thoughts, Hannah also found herself drawn to the park, seeking solace beneath the sheltering branches of the familiar oak tree.

As the sun dipped below the horizon, casting a warm glow over the park, Sarah and Hannah were unwittingly drawn closer to one another. Their eyes met, and in that instant, time seemed to stand still. Words failed them, but their souls felt the rekindling of emotions long forgotten.

A moment of hesitation passed between them, but the love they once shared proved stronger than the walls they had unconsciously built around their hearts. Tearfully, they embraced, their hearts echoing with the bittersweet melodies of past memories and the hope of a renewed connection.

Days turned into weeks, and the space between them filled with long conversations and shared laughter. They weaved stories of their separate journeys, unveiling the trials and triumphs that had shaped them into the individuals they were now. They laughed and cried together, rediscovering the magic that had made their childhood friendship so beautiful.

Through their reunion, Sarah and Hannah learned the power of forgiveness. They allowed the wounds of the past to heal, replaced by a newfound understanding and grace. In forgiving one another, they discovered a profound freedom that only forgiveness can bring.

As their bond grew stronger, Sarah and Hannah realized that the guiding force that had brought them back together was grounded in something greater than themselves. The unbreakable bond of God's love had orchestrated their reunion, nurturing their friendship with a profound sense of purpose.

They saw that God's love was not limited by time or circumstance. It had withstood the test of years and had brought them back to one another when their souls needed it the most. Their friendship became a testament to the enduring power of love, reminding them that even in the darkest of times, there is always hope for reconciliation and renewal.

Sarah and Hannah vowed to cherish their friendship, nurturing it with the understanding that their lives had been intertwined for a reason. They knew that God's love would continue to guide and sustain them as they embarked on a new chapter together.

And so, their story echoed through the city, touching the hearts of those who believed in the power of forgiveness and the unbreakable bond of love. Sarah and Hannah's reunion served as a beautiful reminder that even the most distant friendships can be rekindled, and that God's love has the power to heal wounds and bring hearts back together.

The Resilient Hero

In a small town nestled amidst picturesque mountains, there lived a young boy named Ethan. He possessed a spirit of determination that was unmatched, despite a physical condition that challenged him every step of the way. Ethan was born with a condition that affected his legs, making it difficult for him to walk or run like other children his age. But his indomitable spirit and unwavering faith made him a beacon of resilience.

One sunny day, as Ethan watched a local sports competition from the sidelines, his heart swelled with a longing to participate. He yearned to feel the wind against his face as he raced alongside his friends. Casting his gaze to the sky, he whispered a prayer, "Dear God, please grant me the strength and courage to overcome my challenges. Help me find a way to participate in the sports competition."

Moved by his unwavering faith, God answered Ethan's prayers by placing his trust in the hearts of the townspeople. News of his desire to compete in the sports competition soon reached the ears of Coach Roberts, a retired athlete known for his dedication and belief in the power of resilience. Inspired by Ethan's spirit, the coach decided to train him, teaching him the fundamentals of wheelchair racing.

Days turned into weeks, and under Coach Roberts' guidance, Ethan tirelessly worked to strengthen his upper body, build endurance, and master the art of maneuvering a racing wheelchair. There were moments of frustration and self-doubt, but Ethan's faith in God and his own resilience kept him pushing forward.

The day of the sports competition arrived, and as Ethan rolled up to the starting line, his heart raced with anticipation. His wheelchair gleamed in the sunlight, a symbol of the courage and determination that burned within him.

The crowd watched in awe as Ethan prepared to compete against able-bodied athletes, defying the odds stacked against him.

The whistle blew, and with every ounce of strength, Ethan propelled his wheelchair forward, his determination propelling him faster than he had ever gone before. As he raced down the track, he felt a sense of freedom he had never experienced. His heart soared with each push of the wheels, fueling his belief that anything was possible with resilience and God's grace.

The cheers of the crowd filled his ears, urging him on, as he approached the finish line. With a burst of speed, Ethan crossed the finish line, tears streaming down his face. His radiant smile reflected the triumph of his resilient spirit and his unwavering faith.

In that moment, Ethan realized the true power of perseverance and the strength found in God's grace. He understood that his physical challenges were not limitations but stepping stones to something greater. His journey had taught him that with resilience and faith, he could shatter any barrier that stood in his way.

Ethan's story spread far and wide, inspiring others to overcome their own challenges and find strength in God's grace. He became a symbol of hope for those facing adversity, igniting a flame of resilience and faith within their hearts.

As the years passed, Ethan continued to participate in sports competitions, pushing the boundaries of what was deemed possible. The town regarded him as a true hero, not for his physical accomplishments alone, but for the unwavering spirit that inspired them all.

And so, Ethan's journey of resilience and faith served as a testament to the power of determination and the grace of God. He proved that with the strength found within, one can soar above any challenge and become a beacon of inspiration and hope for others.

The Loving Brothers

In a cozy little neighborhood, nestled among towering trees, lived two brothers named Lucas and Noah. While they shared the same roof and backyard, their personalities couldn't have been more different.

Lucas was practical and focused, always immersed in his books and fascinated by the world of numbers and logic. Noah, on the other hand, had a vivid imagination and a heart full of creativity. He would spend hours exploring the realms of make-believe and crafting stories from thin air.

One sunny afternoon, as they gazed up at the old oak tree that stood at the edge of their yard, an idea sparked within them. They envisioned a magnificent treehouse—a secret hideaway where they could share countless adventures and create memories that would last a lifetime.

Excited by their newfound mission, Lucas and Noah embarked on a journey to build their dream treehouse. Their contrasting personalities soon became apparent, as they approached the task with different perspectives.

Lucas carefully mapped out blueprints and devised a meticulous plan of action. He emphasized the importance of stability, safety, and practicality in the treehouse's construction. Meanwhile, Noah's imagination soared as he envisioned colorful murals, secret trapdoors, and whimsical structures, his focus on creating a space that would spark wonder and joy.

At first, their differences clashed, leading to frustration and disagreements. Lucas viewed Noah's imaginative ideas as unnecessary distractions, while Noah saw Lucas' practicality as stifling creativity. Their hopes of building something magical seemed to be slipping away.

Sensing the tension between them, their parents offered words of wisdom. They reminded Lucas and Noah that their differences were not obstacles but gifts. They encouraged the brothers to appreciate and celebrate each other's unique strengths, for it was through working together that their treehouse would truly become something remarkable.

Awakened by their parents' wisdom, Lucas and Noah approached the task with a fresh perspective. They realized that combining their practicality and creativity would result in a truly special treehouse, one that blended stability and whimsy in perfect harmony.

Lucas took the lead in building a sturdy foundation, ensuring the structure would withstand the test of time. Noah brought his imaginative touch by painting vibrant murals on the walls and adding intricate little details that brought the treehouse to life.

As they worked side by side, the bond between Lucas and Noah grew stronger. They shared laughter, stories, and a sense of accomplishment as their shared vision slowly became a reality. The treehouse became a reflection of their collaboration—a testament to the power of their love as brothers.

When the final nail was hammered and the last brushstroke applied, they stepped back to admire their creation. The treehouse stood tall, a perfect blend of practicality and imagination. It was a place where logic and dreams intertwined, reminding them of the beautiful bond they shared as brothers.

From that day forward, the treehouse became a sanctuary where Lucas and Noah would spend countless hours in joyful play and heartfelt conversations, celebrating their unique strengths and appreciating the balance they brought to one another.

Their story spread through the neighborhood, inspiring others to embrace and celebrate the differences that made them special. Lucas and Noah's treehouse became more than just a physical structure—it became a symbol of the loving bond between two brothers who had learned to appreciate, learn from, and celebrate one another's unique gifts.

And so, Lucas and Noah's treehouse stood as a testament to the power of collaboration, reminding all who ventured inside that we are at our best when we embrace our differences and work together with love and understanding.

Did you love *50 Great Stories For Christian Kids*? Then you should read *Divine armory: Equipping for spiritual battles*[1] by Lily Rosewood!

[2]

Possible ebook description on spiritual warfare:

Title: Divine Armory: Equipping for spiritual battles

Do you feel like you're constantly under attack, facing spiritual battles that drain your energy, steal your joy, and challenge your faith? Are you struggling to discern the sources of darkness in your life and fighting to overcome them? If so, you're not alone. Spiritual warfare is a real and pervasive challenge that every believer faces, yet few know how to navigate it with confidence and victory.

In this ebook, we'll explore the nature of spiritual warfare, its origins, and its manifestations in our lives. We'll discover the weapons that God has given us to fight against the enemy, from the armor of God to the power of prayer and fasting. We'll also explore the tactics of the devil and his minions, exposing their lies, schemes, and deceptions, and learning how to resist and overcome them.

---

1. https://books2read.com/u/4jNogX

2. https://books2read.com/u/4jNogX

Through powerful stories, practical insights, and biblical wisdom, you'll gain a new understanding of the battle for your soul and learn how to stand firm in faith, hope, and love. Whether you're a seasoned warrior or a new believer, this ebook will equip you with the tools and strategies you need to overcome spiritual warfare and live a life of abundant joy, peace, and purpose.

Topics covered:

- The reality of spiritual warfare- The origins and nature of the enemy- The armor of God and other spiritual weapons- The power of prayer and fasting- 50+ powerful biblically supported prayers for all situations- How to increase your spiritual rank

- God's supremacy and sovereignty over the force of darkness- Exposing the tactics of the devil- Walking in faith, hope, and love

Take action now and download this ebook to start your journey toward victory in spiritual warfare. You don't have to fight alone, and you don't have to be defeated. With God on your side and the right tools in your hand, you can conquer the battle for your soul and live a life of purpose, joy, and fulfillment.

Milton Keynes UK
Ingram Content Group UK Ltd.
UKHW020725030823
426269UK00014B/663